SPEAK OF THE

DEVIL

SPEAK

OF

THE

DEVIL

By John Dickson Carr

Introduction and Notes by Tony Medawar

Crippen & Landru, Publishers
Norfolk, Virginia
1994

SPEAK OF THE DEVIL

Copyright © 1994 by Bonita Cron, Mary B. Howes, and
Julia McNiven, Trustee
Introduction copyright © 1994 by Tony Medawar
Cover copyright © by Crippen & Landru Publishers

Cover design and illustration by Deborah Miller
Crippen & Landru logo by Eric D. Greene

Second printing

ISBN (10) – 1-885941-00-5
ISBN (13) – 978-1-885941-00-8

Manufactured in the United States of America

Crippen & Landru Publishers, Inc.
P.O. Box 9315
Norfolk, VA 23505
USA

www.crippenlandru.com
Info@crippenlandru.com

SPEAK OF THE

DEVIL

CONTENTS

DEVILMENT, DUELS, AND INFIDELITY

John Dickson Carr was a consummate writer of the traditional detective story. His work comprises puzzles of motive, puzzles of opportunity and above all puzzles of means; and he is rightly celebrated as master of that most appealing sub-genre, the impossible crime. Yet this supremacy has meant that other aspects of his work are less readily recognised. Specifically, he was among the progenitors of the detective story in a period setting, which accounts for so much crime and mystery writing today.

Whether Carr was *the* progenitor is debatable—others had produced such stories before, principally as pastiches and parodies of Sherlock Holmes—but Carr was the first to write a novel-length historical mystery wherein the period and the puzzle were equally important. At school, Carr had read extensively and developed a love of two periods in the history of England, the country that would become, for much of his life, his adopted home—the Restoration (1660-1685) and around the Regency (the late eighteenth century through the battle of Waterloo). He enjoyed Conan Doyle's historical romances and the work of Alexandre Dumas and Charles Reade and, while he cited G. K. Chesterton and his father as the main influences on his detective fiction generally,[1] these writers were the principal influence on his historical mysteries.

Carr first combined history and mystery in "The Will-o'-the-Wisp," a story published in his school magazine[2] where it was discovered by Douglas Greene. Working late, a lawyer stares sleepily out of his office window at a statue of the Marquis de Lafayette. After apparently blacking out, he finds himself in the first quarter of the eighteenth century as Rupert Brixley, a guest at

---

[1]Kenneth Allsop. "The man who enjoys slapstick with his corpses." *Daily Mail*, 2 August 1961.

[2]*Maroon & White*, Easter 1922.

a reception in Lafayette's honour. Brixley has just been thrown over by a beautiful young woman in favour of an excitable Spaniard who believes his own position is threatened by Lafayette. But Lafayette is more interested in the Will-o'-the-Wisp, a "criminal genius" who has the district in thrall and unexpectedly gatecrashes the reception to challenge the Marquis to a duel. When Brixley sees the Spaniard point a gun at Lafayette, he tries to disarm him. In the struggle, the Wisp is shot instead and the lawyer returns to his office from his "wanderings in the shadow-land of the past."

The story is inevitably naive—Carr was only sixteen—and as in his other tyro works, the characterisation is shallow, and the plot sentimental and melodramatic, in conception as much as execution. Nevertheless, it is important because it foreshadows some of the features of Carr's full-length historical mysteries. Later, at Haverford College (1925-1927), he wrote several historical stories that incorporate elements of mystery. In "The Red Heels," set in 1793, "the ugliest man in France and its greatest lover" dies without learning that his own daughter was responsible for the death of the woman he loved, while the daughter is subsequently denounced by her father's friend at the suggestion of a young artillery officer—who would be known to history as Napoleon I. Only Bonaparte knows precisely what has happened and why, so that the story prefigures the outrageous *Captain Cut-Throat* (1955), in which he is directly responsible for a series of impossible murders among his own troops, massed in Boulogne and awaiting the command to invade England.

Another story written at Haverford, "The Dim Queen," is set in Spain in 1815. A soldier in Napoleon's army is tricked into a duel with a woman who wounds him cruelly; he is eventually shown to have been "the cunningest sword-arm in Europe." "The Inn of the Seven Swords" takes place in 1649 and concerns a plan to rescue King Charles I from London where he awaits execution. The rescue appears to succeed—in the face of history—but a different outcome is revealed in the closing paragraphs. Significantly, "The Inn of the Seven Swords" is among the titles ascribed to Jeff Caldwell, a central character in Carr's penultimate novel, *Deadly Hall*, of whom it is said that, like Carr, "each of your historical novels contains some small element of mystery which is cleared up at the end." Caldwell also explains that he had always wanted to write "swashbuckling stuff, not altogether free of gadzookses or the like, but at least historically accurate" as well as "one other kind of novel . . . detective stories, about who killed whom and why."

When Carr began writing professionally,[3] he concentrated on detective stories with a contemporary setting although, as S. T. Joshi has noted, "History frequently plays a significant part in [these] also. Many of them feature a crime that occurred years before the bulk of the action—a crime that must either be cleared up before the entire case can be laid to rest, or that seems an uncanny precursor to the modern crime."[4] Eventually, the lure of the historical setting became irresistible and, with *Devil Kinsmere*, published in 1934 as by "Roger Fairbairn," Carr produced what he would later describe as a "light historical romance."[5]

But, while Carr was a fine technician in the art of mystery and widely read in the history of the Restoration, he had much to learn as a writer of historical fiction, and we can see how he learned from his youthful errors because, thirty years later, he revised

---

[3]Carr burned his first novel and many other typescripts during his sojourn in Paris in the late 1920s. In Howard Haycraft's *Murder for Pleasure: The Life and Times of the Detective Story* (New York: D. Appleton-Century, 1941) Carr is quoted as describing the lost novel as "a historical romance with lots of Gadzookses and swordplay." While there is no evidence for concluding that it was "a historical-detective chronicle," as suggested by some authorities, Douglas Greene has proposed that some elements of the plot may have been incorporated into *Devil Kinsmere*.

[4]S. T. Joshi. *John Dickson Carr: A Critical Study*. Ohio: Bowling Green State University Popular Press, 1990.

[5]*Sunday Times*, 6 November 1938.

Devil Kinsmere and published it under his own name as *Most Secret*. *Devil Kinsmere* describes events befalling Roderick "Devil" Kinsmere in 1670, as related by his grandson, Major R. B. Kinsmere, during the period of the battle of Waterloo. Arriving in London to claim an inheritance of £500,000—an astronomic amount amended to £90,000 in *Most Secret*—Kinsmere soon finds that the ring given by Charles I to his father is more interesting, and not only to himself. It leads to a meeting with Bygones Abraham, one of two messengers employed by Charles II, and—as happens to the heroes of many of Carr's historical mysteries—a challenge to a duel from the second messenger, Captain Ratty Harker. Harker is murdered and, at the King's behest, Kinsmere replaces him on a mission to France with which Charles is negotiating a secret Treaty. Kinsmere also finds love in Harker's mistress, Dolly Landis.

Carr distinguishes *Devil Kinsmere* from most of his detective stories by revealing the murderer's identity in passing, and there are few if any clues. As in *Captain Cut-Throat*, the real question is the murderer's employer and that person's motives. The book also exemplifies Carr's view that the value of an act lies solely in its effect with the result in *Devil Kinsmere* that, as one character puts it, "the heroes and the villains seem to have got all mixed up. I ain't sure meself just which is which."

The book's shortcomings lie not in the broad canvas against which Carr sets his story, but in relatively minor points even though he partly pre-empted such criticism by stating in the introduction that "some of the details . . . are anachronisms so apparent that not even Major Kinsmere could have pretended to believe them." Nevertheless, they detract little from the pleasure of the book—as one reviewer commented smugly, "'The story,' Mr Fairbairn adds in a specious 'editor's note,' 'is given as it was told and the reader may be left to determine how much is fact, how much fiction and how much wild absurdity.' The common reader will probably not attempt to determine these delicate questions while those who know enough to check the historical accuracy of Mr Fairbairn's setting will probably not read his 'rowdy chronicle,' which means that everybody ought to be satisfied."[6]

For *Most Secret*, Carr assiduously revised the language throughout and made the novel tighter. He also corrected the anachronisms—no longer did Kinsmere saunter along "with his hands in his pockets" or say "Hi" and "What, ho"—and he sharpened the characters of Dolly Landis and Ratty Harker: As Pembroke Harker, the messenger is made more cruel and contemptible, probably to align him with the Earl of Pembroke whom Carr suspected of *The Murder of Sir Edmund Godfrey*, while Dolly is brighter and less submissive to Harker and therefore more worthy of Kinsmere's attention. The "Big Hat" becomes the "plotter-in-chief," Kinsmere's father is "Buck" rather than "Beauty," and "Devil" becomes "Rowdy" and less of the puerile bumpkin of the original who has to be admonished for "making faces at people . . . and uttering strange noises." A careless mis-naming of Nell Gwyn's[7] first "protector," specifically criticised in one review, is corrected and, whereas the narrative in *Devil Kinsmere* breaks off because of the arrival of the news of the victory at Waterloo, Carr pointedly remarks in *Most Secret* that "Colonel Kinsmere did not break off because he was interrupted by news of the victory. News of the victory did not reach England until three days later. He broke off because in the telling of the final part on Sunday, June 18th, he drank too much . . . ."

In *The Murder of Sir Edmund Godfrey* (1936), Carr produced an ingenious amalgam of the detective story and the academic treatise. The death in 1678 of Godfrey and its possible connection

---

[6]*Times Literary Supplement*, 18 October 1934.

[7]Carr planned but never wrote a one-hour radio play entitled *Charles and Nelly*, which he described as "a long cherished notion: Charles II and Nelly Gwyn, with period speech and music."

with the infamous Popish Plot against the Catholics was G. K. Chesterton's "favourite murder in real life"[8] with all the features of "a really good detective story . . . the presence of clues that are not clues . . . and, as the romancer could easily introduce characters like Titus Oates and Shaftesbury and Charles the Second and Pepys, he could have a high old time."[9] Carr did just that, producing a monumental study that sets a carefully reasoned analysis of the facts within a meticulously researched framework of living characters. His exhaustive analysis of the evidence and all the possible solutions make it a model for books of its kind.

A few years later, shortly after Carr began the radio serial that forms this volume, he and his wife "were seated in their living room, reading, when they heard a whistle, a heavy hiss and a series of thunderclap concussions and then found themselves on the floor, blinded by dust. The first thing Carr noticed when he got up was that they now had an uninterrupted yiew of their garden . . . the house was almost a total wreck."[10] It was September 1940 and Hitler's *Luftwaffe* were bombing London.

The Carrs had a miraculous escape, as did the five completed episodes of *Speak of the Devil* which Carr had to salvage from the rubble. They withdrew to Bristol where the *Luftwaffe* soon finished off the last remnants of their furniture and Carr's precious collection of books. After evacuating his family to a safer part of England and being bombed out of the Savage Club in London, Carr lodged himself in Devon to complete various projects, including *Speak of the Devil*.

When the serial was broadcast during February and March

---

[8]G. K. Chesterton. "The case of Sir Edmund Godfrey," *The Strand*, February 1927.

[9]*Ibid.*

[10]Robert Lewis Taylor. "Two authors in an attic." *The New Yorker*, 8 and 15 September 1951.

1941, Carr was delighted by "the slickness with which everything moves, the conveying of atmosphere above all. Down here in this neglected spot, they queue up to hear it. One formidable maiden lady passed the comment: 'It's odd how you seem to be seeing it as well as hearing it.' I stifled my impulse to reply 'Madam, if you knew how hard the producer and the author worked to achieve that effect, you wouldn't think it was so bloody odd.'"[11] Although no recordings survive, the serial has a vibrancy of its own.[12]

Four years later, Carr incorporated the central mystery of the serial into *She Slept Lightly*, a stage play set during the battle of Waterloo in typically Carrian surroundings, "an ancient windmill, gaunt stone, its sails tattered." The play is inevitably more narrowly focused than the serial, but what little is lost by the compression of the story is more than compensated by the threatening and claustrophobic atmosphere that the setting and the writing achieve.

Carr wrote other wholly original radio mysteries with historical settings. "Lord of the Witch Doctors," as by Robert Southwell,[13] is set in Zanzibar in 1889 and involves the thwarting by the British Resident of a German plot to murder the Sultan. "Death in the Desert" is set on board a paddle steamer on the Nile in the winter of 1895, and incorporates elements from the contemporary detective story *My Late Wives* while the solution of the mystery foreshadows *Papa Là-bas*. In "The Body Snatchers,"

---

[11]Letter from Carr to Val Gielgud, no date (February 1941). BBC Archives.

[12]The text presented is not the version as broadcast, which is lost. However, it is believed to differ only in one small respect—in Carr's words, "on page 6 of episode 5, I find I have made a slight historical error. The bodies of convicted criminals were not buried in quicklime but handed over to the surgeons for dissection." The error was corrected before the broadcast.

[13]Almost certainly named for Sir Robert Southwell, Clerk of the Council in the court of Charles II.

set in 1833, a gang of resurrectionists' efforts to satisfy a doctor's request for a corpse result in an investigation by a "Peeler"called Stalker. The play is dark and atmospheric, conveying the period well notwithstanding the limitations of the medium. However, the radio play "He Who Whispers" was set in a dressing-room backstage at a London music-hall in 1890 so that there was little need to create any sense of the period.

As with Carr's novels, history plays an important part in many of his other radio plays, which include variations on two mysteries described by Dumas. "The Scandalous Affair of the Queen's Necklace," set in Paris in 1784, is based on the theft of the necklace given by Louis XV to the *Comtesse* Du Barry. While in "The Man in the Iron Mask," set partly in 1703 but mainly in 1669, Carr proposed a new if improbable solution. *Devil Kinsmere* is revisited as Charles II attempts to dupe Louis XIV of France while negotiating the Secret Treaty of Dover but is outwitted by the French Foreign Minister and France's Ambassador to England.

Carr's first historical novel under his own name was *The Bride of Newgate* (1950), set like *Speak of the Devil* during the Regency and beginning on 21 August 1815, three days after the grandson of Devil Kinsmere broke off his narration. The following morning, Dick Darwent will hang for killing Lord Francis Orford in a duel. Orford, like Sir Edmund Godfrey, was run through with a sword but the clean soles of his shoes showed that, also like Godfrey, his body had been brought to the place where it was found from elsewhere. Darwent claims he is innocent and that, on the night of the murder, he was taken by a seemingly spectral coach-man to Orford's "house near Kinsmere" where he saw his body in a room where it is later proved the murder could not have taken place—a claim similar to one made by a "witness" in the investigation into Godfrey's murder. Darwent's intended fate also recalls Samuel Atkins, Samuel Pepys' clerk, who was arrested in connection with Godfrey's murder and escaped hanging only at the eleventh hour.

Freed after his conviction is quashed, Darwent determines to

discover the truth. As often in Carr's work—regardless of the setting—he is torn between two women: Lady Caroline Ross who
married him in prison to circumvent the terms of her grandfather's
will; and Dolly Spencer, an actress not unlike Dolly Landis of
Devil Kinsmere. Darwent also has more than his fair share of
duels but his most serious dilemma is resolved by the timely death
of one of the "dear charmers," and the novel has been criticised for
ending happily and immorally—the murderer is not charged because the victim, a moneylender known as "Caliban,"[14] deserved to
die.

In an appendix to *The Bride of Newgate,* Carr noted that "No
famous historical character appears in the story at all. Many are
talked about. But they are seen at a distance—on a balcony, or in
an opera box—so that they never speak and never enter to clog up
the action." He must have relented in this view for real people are
central to his next historical mystery, *The Devil in Velvet* (1951),
unquestionably one of his finest novels. Period detail and plot are
seamlessly woven together, and there is none of the carelessness
of *Devil Kinsmere* nor any of the pedantry and sciolism that stiffen
and mar some of the later historical mysteries.

However, the novel is more than simply a detective story set
in an earlier age. Its plot is elaborated within an extraordinary and
ambiguous framework of fantasy. Nicholas Fenton has long
dreamed of being carried back into the past of his family's London
home. Through an apparent compact with the Devil, he barters his
soul as the price of being transported forever from 1925 to 1675
into the body of his own ancestor, Sir Nicholas Fenton, so that he
can prevent the poisoning of Fenton's wife. For "nine dim years,"
Fenton has "cherished idealistically a bad engraving" of Lady
Lydia but, once in her time, finds himself torn between her and her
cousin who proves to be the only person he told of his deal with

---

[14]A pen-name used by Carr at Haverford College.

the Devil. Under the watchful eye of Lydia's chambermaid Judith Pamphlin—named for Sir Edmund Godfrey's housekeeper—the Professor sets about his pre-emptive investigation, using his historian's knowledge to survive the rigours of the age and broadening his objective from his home where he must detect the enemy within to the wider world and the Popish Plot. But Lydia dies, and his attempt to forestall Lord Shaftesbury and his fellow conspirators by warning Charles II of their intentions fails spectacularly when his claim to foretell the future leads to accusations of treason and witchcraft.

But, it is not certain that Carr really intended the reader to accept that Professor Fenton is actually transported into the past or even the existence of the Devil who appears when the "frail" Fenton is dosed heavily with chloral hydrate and is neither seen nor heard, at least not in any conventional sense—"only that unstable ever-varying outline and . . . soundless words." Furthermore, the shift in time occurs while Fenton sleeps after blacking out on a whiskey and soda to which he added "an overly generous dose" of chloral. Unlike characters in two later novels, *Fear is the Same* and *Fire, Burn!*, who are also shifted into the past, Fenton's transition is permanent. This is consistent with the premise of the compact, but another explanation may lie in "The Dead Man's Knock," the last of Carr's historical mysteries for radio.

In this play, during an argument with his wife Margery and her lover, Professor Edward Kynaston is shifted from 1954 to 1796 in order to learn who murdered a woman who looked like Margery in a "vast powder-scented house called Widestairs." Kynaston is ill and once said he'd "give half [his] life to know who killed" Lady Helen Loring of whom he too has long cherished "a coloured engraving." There are three suspects, including Lord Liverpool who became British Prime Minister in 1812 after Spencer Perceval was assassinated. The murder is explained—albeit obliquely—but it transpires that Kynaston was killed by his wife's lover during the argument and that the rest of the play was simply "a fantasy" of the narrator, Carr's ubiquitous man in black.

Did Fenton dream or die? Or did he really whistle up the Devil? Carr certainly implies that the shift in time in *The Devil in Velvet* is unreal because characters ascribe a devastating speech against Shaftesbury to the real Sir Nick Fenton when, as the Professor makes plain, the speech would in reality be given by Lord Halifax some years later. Of course, this riddle is insoluble. We know only that, at the end of the novel, Fenton's "mind and soul were at peace . . . in this age he had found what he sought."

Fear is the Same (1956) is a story of parallel murder and parallel murderers with the playwright Richard Brindsley Sheridan and the Prince Regent playing key roles. It begins as a conventional historical novel, but one of the characters, Miss Jennifer Baird, is not what she appears to be. Together with her lover, the Earl of Glenarvon[15]—otherwise known as Phil Maddern, a contender for the World Middleweight Boxing title—she has been shifted from 1945 to 1795. He has become an earlier holder of the earldom and master of Widestairs, a house in London, while she is now betrothed to a loathsome wimp whose first recourse whenever anything goes wrong is his father. Something fearful hung over the lovers in their own time, and the shift occurred when Jennifer "cried out and said 'Oh, if only we could be out of this! If only we could go back 150 years in time and forget it!' . . . A little voice, inside my head, I don't know where from, whispered to me and said 'Would it be any different; if you did go back?'" A little voice? Professor Fenton's "visitor" again? Perhaps, but the whole of the novel takes place in an instant in 1945 and, as the lovers have not been involved in any accident or taken any kind of drug, nor do they retain any of their physical injuries when they return

---

[15]In "Till the Great Armadas Come," a radio play set during the 'little blitz' of 1944, another Lord Glenarvon, a doctor and so not the hero of *Fear is the Same*, is involved in an attempt to prevent the devastation of London.

to their own time, neither they nor the reader can decide what has really happened.

Fire, Burn! (1957) was the first novel in a trilogy on the development of Scotland Yard. Jack Cheviot, Superintendent of the Murder Squad, steps out of a taxi he boarded in the early 1950s to find himself in 1829. He too has dreamed of the past—as he is reminded by "a satiric voice" in his own brain. "Isn't this only the other part of your dream? . . . Didn't you want to see, in action, the first Scotland Yard? . . . Didn't you want to amaze them by solving some such mystery, with fingerprints or ballistics or modern deduction?"—and he has a confused and selective memory of his own time—he cannot remember his parents' names nor if he was married, yet he recognises Lady Flora Drayton, a beautiful widow who appears to be his lover, from "a picture book . . . to be exact, from a folio of coloured drawings" in the Victoria and Albert Museum. Cheviot has been shifted in time alone and, although everyone calls him by his own name, he cannot have become one of his own ancestors because "not one had lived in London for eight or nine generations." Cheviot is asked by the first Police Commissioners to investigate a seemingly trivial matter that develops startlingly into a "an accursed drawing-room game of who-killed-who-and-how." He also has to overcome prejudice and hatred of the "Peelers," which leads to a challenge to a duel and, eventually, to his own murder. However, almost immediately afterwards, we learn that the mystery took place inside Cheviot's mind after he was knocked senseless when the taxi in which he was travelling was involved in an accident—Flora Drayton had the name and face of his own wife! In addition to a clever if questionable solution to the impossible crime involved, the novel presents a convincing and detailed portrait of Georgian London and places lost to later generations.

After the Second World War, the historical mysteries and especially the chronicles of shifted time, enabled Carr to escape from what one of his characters termed the "damnation of progress"[16] and to experience vicariously the facets of the past that so appealed to him, the morals and conventions of the times when men were gentlemen (or rogues) and women were women in all their variety. Importantly, they also allowed him to explore new possibilities in the field of impossible crime. While only one of his contemporary detective stories written after 1953—*Dark of the Moon* (1967)—featured a solution that he had not already used in a radio play or short story, almost all of the historical mysteries are original even if some of the devices that confuse and perplex the Bow Street Runners and others, for example in *Fire, Burn!* and *The Demoniacs*, would have been literally impossible in a contemporary setting.

The second book in Carr's Scotland Yard trilogy, *Scandal at High Chimneys* (1959), is set in 1865. For the first time in one of his novels, the detective is a real person, ex-Inspector Jonathan Whicher who resigned to become a private investigator after the mishandling of the investigation into the case of Constance Kent. In its dark mood and largely confined settings, this "Victorian melodrama" is reminiscent of his 1932 novel *Poison in Jest*, but the book is marred by Carr's tendency to parade his sources. Thus, while one critic found the novel a "brilliant evocation" of the period, another commented that Carr "relentlessly trots out all he has ever mugged up about the Victorian underworld as though nobody had ever read *Fanny by Gaslight* or heard of Mayhew, which the hero quotes with date, publisher's name and page number in the course of conversation in the same way that his light lady quotes fourteen lines of Esmond all by heart." Like all of Carr's novels set after the Regency, *Scandal at High Chimneys* is a pure detective story with little of the perilous adventures that invigorate the mysteries set before this date. Disappointingly, the solution to the murders is weak for, though clever and feasible, it

---

[16]Quoted from *Night at the Mocking Widow.*

stretches belief more than a little and the reader's obfuscation is largely due to an improbable misunderstanding.

Real people—namely Edgar A. Poe and John Wilkes Booth—also play detective in two short stories, "The Gentleman from Paris" (1950) and "The Black Cabinet" (1951). Both stories work because the milieux, respectively New York in 1849 and Paris in 1858, are carefully described and the detective's identity is withheld until the last line to provide an additional and surprisingly irrelevant surprise, rather than an incessant distraction as is often the case in this type of mystery.

The last in the Scotland Yard trilogy was *The Witch of the Low-Tide* (1961), an "Edwardian melodrama" set in 1907 which has been criticised for lacking period detail, so much so that S. T. Joshi has suggested that "it hardly deserves to be considered a historical detective story at all." The novel has a flavour of the period but the charge is fair, and Carr is again guilty of parading trivia that are an unwanted distraction from a clever plot and an ingenious locked room, albeit somewhat similar to the problem in the second Sir Henry Merrivale novel, *The White Priory Murders* (1934).

The Demoniacs has been described as "Book 1 of the Scotland Yard *quartet*"[17] because the central character, Jeffrey Wynne, is a thief-taker, "one of those who most stealthily are called 'Mr Fielding's people,'" later known as the Bow Street Runners. The novel is set in 1757 and prominent roles are played by Fielding himself and the Reverend Laurence Sterne, author of *Tristram Shandy*. The story begins on London Bridge, which has not yet fallen down and is marvellously realised as a derelict, dark and dangerous place. There is sudden death, and Wynne has to protect

---

[17]Geoff Webster. *An analytical chart of the stories of John Dickson Carr* (Unpublished typescript).

the woman he loves and himself from the agents of her father's mistress who—inexplicably—appear determined to kill them. As with the previous novel and several of his other novels, Carr's catchpenny title is of little relevance and the murder, though clever and acceptable for the period, is unsuccessful because Wynne has no basis for deducing that the apparent death from supernatural causes is in fact murder nor for his inspired deduction of the actual means.

Papa Là-bas, The Ghosts' High Noon, and *Deadly Hall* are set in the United States, which formed the setting for some of Carr's contemporary novels and a few short stories. These include the early "The Other Hangman" (1935) set in Carr's native Pennsylvania in the early 1890s and, intentionally or not, very much in the style of Melville Davisson Post with a shrewdly observed picture of small town politics and a powerful if uncomfortable plot. The New Orleans trilogy—and references in the second and third book to the crime in the preceding volume confirm that they are part of the same history—are usually dismissed but, regardless of their merit as novels, they are valuable for the insight they give into Carr as a writer. In the names of characters, details of settings and in other ways, there are subtle references to his earlier work including the stories he wrote at school and at college. The autobiographical qualities of the hero of *Deadly Hall* have been noted, while *The Ghosts' High Noon*—named for a novel by Carolyn Wells, one of Carr's favourite authors when he was a boy—opens with a vignette of Harpers, his U. S. publisher, and Washington, D. C. in 1912, which the "Notes for the Curious" record was once the home of "W. N. Carr of Pennsylvania, his wife and their small but noisy son."

The historical settings are generally well drawn, especially in *Papa Là-Bas* (1968) but the three books are nevertheless very much the work of a writer whose powers are progressively declining. *Papa Là-Bas* is set in 1858 and the detective is another real person, Judah P. Benjamin, who held key posts in the short-lived Confederate administration and escaped to England after the South lost. By improbable garrulity, the murderer effectively identifies himself while his murder method is extraordinarily risky, and the person responsible for the first "miracle" is rightly accused of "a tendency to make mysteries for the sake of making mysteries"—a charge as easily levelled at Carr and not only in this book. People frequently act irrationally and their tendency to begin to make some important revelation and then break off suddenly has been criticised so often that further comment is unnecessary. The impossible crime in *The Ghosts' High Noon* (1969), set in 1912, is similar to that of *A Graveyard to Let* and, therefore, not difficult to detect—once the "miracle" is solved, the guilty party is immediately apparent when, without the miracle, detection would have been harder. In fact, although tantamount to sacrilege, several of Carr's novels would surely have been even better detective stories if they hadn't featured impossible crimes. *Deadly Hall* (1971), set in 1927, concludes the trilogy with a riddle of missing bullion and a murder with echoes of a device used in an earlier novel; however, the murderer's motivation for adopting an uncertain and needlessly mysterious method is wholly unconvincing.

Wilkie Collins plays detective in Carr's last novel, *The Hungry Goblin* (1972), set in Victorian England. The worst aspect of this bad book—worse than the acutely improbable plot—is the fact that Carr makes little if any effort to convey the setting with token references to Victorian buildings and people, and anachronistic speech and behaviour throughout. As in other late books, some characters display a peculiar tendency to address each other by nicknames or by names other than their own. Jenny the "succubus" becomes Muriel but prefers to be known as Cathy, while the genuine Muriel becomes Jenny but adopts the nickname of Sapphire. The psychology is logical but the effect is confusing. Even Wilkie Collins is addressed variously as "auctorial sage," "*Moonstone*," "master of mystery" and even "friend of *The Woman in White.*" The clumsily handled impossible crime is recycled from *The Exploits of Sherlock Holmes* in which, together with Doyle's son, Carr had produced enjoyable palimpsests of the adventures of his favourite detective. Furthermore, while Carr's open and warmly appreciative attitude to sex and sexuality is refreshing and plausible in the majority of his novels, in some—especially towards the end of his career—it is immature and frankly obsessive, exemplified by *The Hungry Goblin* in which a woman swaps places with a friend and her husband is suspicious only because "her amatory pattern" is "so devilishly and wonderfully varied" that it can't be the same "beloved girl." The novel is a sad epitaph.

When John Dickson Carr died in 1977, a number of projects were left unfinished, including a memoir of the Golden Age of Detective Fiction and at least one more historical mystery that would have featured another celebrated writer and amateur investigator as its detective. None of these typescripts survive. However, through the enterprise of Douglas Greene who has introduced us to so much of Carr's less well-known work, we have the opportunity to read something very special—a previously unpublished full-length historical mystery, imbued with the spirit of the Regency and posing as damnable a riddle as any elsewhere.

But come, let John Dickson Carr, the King of Misdirection, speak for himself. It is twenty to seven on the tenth of February 1941. You are listening to the Home Service of the British Broadcasting Corporation. The *News in Norwegian* has just ended. *Speak of the Devil* is about to begin . . .

Tony Medawar
Brussels, 1994

SPEAK OF THE DEVIL

THE CHARACTERS

Captain Hugh Austen	Of the Grenadier Guard
Lady Cynthia Mercer	Woman about Town
Thomas Tring	Man about Town
Mary Adair	The Unknown
Dr. Horatio Cameron	The Man in Black
Elias Godfrey	Lawyer
Georges Pepotin	Aeronaut
Prinny	H. R. H., The Prince Regent
Ensign Johnny Brisbane	Ninety-Fifth Rifles
The Three Dandies	Greek Chorus
Joe Manton	Of Manton's Shooting Gallery
A Bow Street Runner	
A Waiter	

(Incidental voices for lackeys, attendants, and so on)

Setting: Regency England, 1816.

EPISODE 1

NARRATOR: Now the story goes that in London of long ago—to be exact, in the year eighteen hundred and sixteen—a man made a wager which was the talk of St. James's. And it must be an extravagant wager to startle St. James's in the year eighteen hundred and sixteen. For this was the age of the bucks and the dandies, of the gamesters and the duelists, of the coaching-road and the prize ring. It was an age of fine manners and boisterous drinking, when Boney had been beaten at Waterloo only a year before. When gentlemen in tall hats sauntered down St. James's Street, or lounged in the bow window at White's. When ladies in poke bonnets ate ices at Vauxhall Gardens, or danced the waltz at Almack's, or gossiped of the fall of Beau Brummell and the scandal of Lord Byron. When Tom Cribb was champion of England. When that new miracle, gaslight, had begun to flicker in the cobblestoned streets. When already the balloon and the steamboat were commonplace sights. When, in short, progress was carrying us to the Devil. The center of fashion in this hiccuping age was Carlton House, residence of His Royal Highness, the Prince Regent. Here, in the gold drawing room, among the banked flowers, walked "Prinny" himself: now an ageing and bloated grandee, but still the First Gentleman of Europe. So the story goes that one night, when His Royal Highness was entertaining a group of merry guests. . .

(The voice fades. Through the foregoing we have faintly

heard the strains of "Auprès de ma Blonde," which now rise more loudly for a second or two, and then fade, We hear the murmur of a crowd of people; muttered voices, laughter, and then, out of it, the voices of three dandies, all drawling, whinnying, and affected.)

FIRST DANDY (*with a flicker of interest*): Damme, here's something odd! Have you seen this handbill?

SECOND DANDY (*languidly*): No, old boy. Some filthy beggar tried to give me one when I came in, but I wouldn't have it. Cursed impudence.

THIRD DANDY: What does it say?

FIRST DANDY: "The public are respectfully reminded that tomorrow, the 16th June, in Vauxhall Gardens, the noted aeronaut Monsieur Georges Pepotin will not only make a public ascent by air balloon—"

SECOND DANDY: Dull, old boy. Intolerably dull. It's never worth seeing unless they catch fire.

FIRST DANDY: Listen! " —will not only make a public ascent by air balloon, but will attempt a descent from the balloon in a (*hesitates over the word*) parachute of his own design—"

SECOND DANDY: That's not new either. Word of honor! I remember some Frenchie tried it when I was a little boy. Went up from South Audley Street, and came down slap in a field back of St. Pancras Church.

THIRD DANDY: Wait a bit. What's a (*giving the word its full French pronunciation*) parachute?

SECOND DANDY: It's a great big thing like an umbrella, made out of canvas. There was a basket hung underneath, with the Frenchman in it. (*With some animation and amusement*) Damme, you should have seen it! The contraption swung so much that sometimes the basket swung clear up to the roof, and we thought the Frenchman was going to be shot out like a demnition catapult. (*Disconsolately*) He wasn't, though.

FIRST DANDY: Not killed?

SECOND DANDY: No, old boy. Only a knock on the clinker, and came up swearing.

THIRD DANDY (*musingly*): Parachute.

FIRST DANDY: Do you think this thing tomorrow night might be worth a visit? I mean, seeing the fellow go shooting out of the basket and land half way to Newmarket—?

THIRD DANDY (*excitedly*): Gad, I remember now! I thought it sounded familiar. Tring's going up in that balloon.

FIRST DANDY (*aroused*): Not Tommy Tring?

THIRD DANDY (*with gossiping hurry*): Tommy Tring. I heard about it at Alvanley's last night. An awful drum: everybody was there.

SECOND DANDY (*incredulously*): Tommy Tring is going to flop out of the balloon in a demnition parachute?

THIRD DANDY: No, no, he's only going in the car of the balloon. (*Greedily*) Come close and listen. Oh, Tommy was in rare spirits last night! He's quite a friend of mine, you know; gave me his arm from one end of Bond Street to the other last Tuesday week—

FIRST DANDY (*impatiently*): Yes, yes; go on.

THIRD DANDY: Tommy said he knew all about earthly Venuses, so he might as well examine the spots on the heavenly one. (*Chuckles*) Oh, yes. And he also made us laugh fit to burst with a story about a fellow named

Austen—Captain Austen—

SECOND DANDY (*faintly interested*): Damme, I've heard that story. Austen. He's mad, ain't he? Completely out of his head?

FIRST DANDY: Sh-h!

SECOND DANDY: Why "Sh-h," old boy?

FIRST DANDY: That's Captain Austen over there now.

THIRD DANDY (*excitedly*): Where?

FIRST DANDY: On that red settee, by the rose vases. Cynthia Mercer's with him.

THIRD DANDY (*rapturously*): Lady Cynthia Mercer?

SECOND DANDY (*musingly*): Now just what is our lovely Cynthia doing with Captain Austen? The whole town knows that she's Tommy Tring's—

FIRST DANDY: Sh-h!

SECOND DANDY: My tongue's my own, old boy. If any fellow don't like it, he can call for satisfaction.

THIRD DANDY: They're looking at us. I wonder what they're saying?

(A few bars of "Auprès de ma Blonde," which fade into Hugh Austen's voice. It is a full, rather hard voice, of a man in his early thirties.)

AUSTEN: You have courage, my dear Cynthia.

(Cynthia Mercer's voice suggests very much the woman of the world: thirtyish, poised, intelligent, but with a good deal of underlying passion and emotion.)

CYNTHIA: Courage? Why?

AUSTEN (*grimly*): To be seen in public with such a notoriously unbalanced person as myself.

CYNTHIA: Hugh, please!

AUSTEN: I hate to be laughed at, Cynthia.

CYNTHIA: They're not laughing at *you*, my dear.

AUSTEN: No? Look at those three exquisites over there—quizzing-glasses and all. And look there, in that group by the stairs: the very fat Humpty Dumpty with the enormous shirt collar—

CYNTHIA (*in an agitated whisper*): Hugh, for heaven's sake! That's the Prince Regent.

AUSTEN (*as though enlightened*): Indeed. (*Under his breath*) Sir, I crave your pardon. (*Aloud*) He seems indifferently sober.

CYNTHIA: He is The First Gentleman of Europe. (*In a hurry*) Hugh, listen to me. He will probably come over here in a moment—

AUSTEN: Oh, yes. You must tell me how to behave. Remember, I am not in the habit of moving in such exalted circles as these.

CYNTHIA (*paying no attention*): If he's in a good humor, he'll give you his hand to kiss. You only pretend to kiss it, like kissing the Bible in court.

AUSTEN: Thereby showing at the same time my respect for royalty, and my sturdy British independence. The genius of compromise, Cynthia.

CYNTHIA (*breathlessly, paying no attention to irony*): He will probably notice your Guard's uniform, and ask if you were at the battle of Waterloo. If he says he was at Waterloo and led the Guards there, for heaven's sake don't contradict him. He's awfully sensitive about that.

AUSTEN: (*Laughs*)

CYNTHIA (*suddenly very much on her dignity*): I think you forget your manners, Captain Austen.

AUSTEN: I do, madam. Again you must remember that I'm

a low fellow. In private life, a mere schoolmaster.

CYNTHIA (*sharply*): *Must* you harp on that?

AUSTEN: Yes.

CYNTHIA (*almost storming at him*): You're an *impossible* fellow; that's what you are. I can't think why I take so much trouble with you, unless it's because (*laying it on thick*) I have the misfortune to—to feel some affection for you, if you *must* make me say it. And you repay me with behavior that would disgrace a bear.

AUSTEN (*sincerely*): I'm sorry.

CYNTHIA: There, now: that's better!

AUSTEN (*vaguely*): You see, sometimes I—

CYNTHIA (*gently*): You're hurt, Hugh. You were hurt in the head at Waterloo.

AUSTEN: And so *you* think I'm mad too?

CYNTHIA (*urgently*): I think you imagine things, Hugh. You imagined this girl—this girl (*contemptuously*) you say you're in love with. She never existed; please believe that.

AUSTEN: I tell you, I talked with her! I talked with her at the Richmonds' ball, three nights before Waterloo. I touched her. I—

CYNTHIA: Yes?

AUSTEN: She gave me this miniature. Look!

CYNTHIA: I've seen the miniature. But you don't know her name?

AUSTEN: No.

CYNTHIA: Does anyone else know her name?

AUSTEN: No.

CYNTHIA: Can anyone identify her face, even though you have a picture of her on that miniature?

AUSTEN (*bitterly, after a pause*): No.

CYNTHIA: Oh, Hugh, do be a sensible boy! For a year . . . a year . . . you've done nothing but search for this mythical lost love of yours. You've questioned every person who was at the ball that night. You've spent a year's wages questioning servants. Does anyone know this mysterious girl? Has anyone ever seen her? No! Yet you persist in—

AUSTEN (*calmly*): Yes.

CYNTHIA: At first I thought she might be some scullery wench dressed up in borrowed clothes—

AUSTEN: My God, if it were only as easy as that!

CYNTHIA: —but I've made inquiries myself, and I know she isn't. She's a dream, Hugh. Don't you know what happened to you at Hougoumont? You were wounded in the head, and dragged out of the fire. Yes, touch the scar: touch it!

AUSTEN (*with ironical gravity*): If you fan yourself any harder, Cynthia, you'll break the fan.

CYNTHIA: Never mind my fan. You do know you're the laughing stock of London, don't you? You know what Mr. Tring is saying about you at every dinner table?

AUSTEN (*quietly*): Ah, yes. I hear the famous Mr. Thomas Tring has been very witty at my expense. I can't imagine why. I have never had the honor of meeting the gentleman—

CYNTHIA: Oh, you donkey! (*Primly*) Some people might say it was because he found me not unattractive. Some people do find me attractive, you know.

AUSTEN: Are we likely to meet Mr. Tring here tonight?

CYNTHIA: Probably. (*With quick suspicion*) Why?

AUSTEN (*agreeably*): I hope to have the extreme pleasure of knocking his teeth down his throat.
(*There is a pause, after which Cynthia speaks in a sharp, alert, common sense voice.*)
CYNTHIA: You don't mean that?
AUSTEN: No? Why not?
CYNTHIA (*with furious earnestness*): You can't do it! You mustn't do it! You mustn't even think of it!
AUSTEN: I repeat, why not?
CYNTHIA (*distractedly*): Oh, dear, I have got into trouble with my tame bear. (*Breaking off*) Listen, Hugh. Tommy Tring has never been beaten at *anything*.
AUSTEN: No?
CYNTHIA: He's fought I don't know how many duels, and never had a scratch. He laughs and laughs, and everybody gives way to him. He can be cool when everybody else is in a flurry—
AUSTEN: Can he, now?
CYNTHIA: He won't argue with you. He'll only . . . step on you.
AUSTEN: So! (*Thoughtfully, with real interest*) Tell me something, Cynthia. Did you have me invited here tonight in the *hope* of seeing a fight?
CYNTHIA (*outraged*): Hugh! How can you say any such a thing!
AUSTEN (*amusedly*): You should see yourself in a mirror, my dear. Your eyes are shining, and your cheeks are flushed, and . . . (*Breaking off*) . . . What is it now?
CYNTHIA: Tommy Tring.
AUSTEN: Where?
CYNTHIA: There. Speaking to the Prince now. The tall,

slender man in brown, with the snuffbox in his hand.
(*With real fear*) Hugh, they're coming over here!

AUSTEN: So I notice.

CYNTHIA: Please listen to me (*Wheedlingly*) Perhaps I *was*
a wee bit naughty in—in coming here with you. But I've
changed my mind; truly and honestly. I have! We *can't*
have anything dreadful happen. It would ruin me. And I
do like you; I declare, I'm almost in love with you—
there!—and, oh, Hugh, you must promise me you won't
. . . (*She breaks off to address another person. Her voice
takes on a note of ineffable sweetness and submission.*)
Your Royal Highness! What an unexpected pleasure!
(*The Prince Regent has a fat, rather throaty voice, with
an immense loftiness of manner, as though he could
hardly get his words over his shirt collar. His manner is
arch and indulgent. He is drunk, but this only adds to his
dignity, and his fluency is impaired only occasionally,
hardly noticeably, by a very slight hiccup.*)

THE PRINCE: Your obedient servant, Lady Cynthia. I am
delighted with you—delighted. (*Lyrically*) Haven't I said,
Tring, that of all the beauteous roses in the garden, our
Cynthia was the fairest to be born without a (*hiccup*)
thorn?

CYNTHIA: And Mr. Tring, I do declare!
(*No reply.*)

THE PRINCE: Speak up, old boy. Don't stand there and
smile. Cynthia, I don't know this other gentleman. Pray
present him to me.

CYNTHIA: Your Highness's very loyal subject, Captain
Austen of the Second Foot Guards. And . . . Captain
Austen, Mr. Tring.

(*Tring speaks. He has a thin, smooth, "smiling" voice: the voice of a man so absolutely sure of himself that he has no need to bother what anyone thinks of him or what he does.*)

TRING: I have heard of Captain Austen. Your servant, sir.

AUSTEN: Yours to command, sir.

THE PRINCE (*affably, with rich satisfaction*): Your uniform, Captain, commends itself to our (*hiccup*) attention. (*With concern*) Damme, Captain, aren't you well? You're as white as a ghost!

TRING (*pleasantly*): Captain Austen is merely in love.

THE PRINCE (*relishing a joke*): So I am informed.

TRING: It's appropriate that Captain Austen should be as white as a ghost. Isn't that so, sir?

CYNTHIA (*warningly*): Hugh!

TRING (*smoothly*): If Your Royal Highness will ask Captain Austen to show you the miniature he is now hiding behind his back, you will see a picture of the lady. Er— may I have the miniature?

AUSTEN: No

TRING: No? But why not?

AUSTEN: Because I don't want you to have it.

TRING (*surprised*): Your wishes, sir, can be of no possible interest to His Highness. The miniature, please.

AUSTEN (*through his teeth*): Cynthia, I warned you . . .

TRING (*changing his tone, laughing*): Cynthia, did you ever see such a complete picture of mortification as our gallant captain? He looks as though I might take it from him, like a doll in a nursery. (*Consolingly*) Come, sir, don't sulk! We won't force you against your will.

THE PRINCE (*in a slight huff*): Certainly not. Though my

friend Tring has told me a story which I considered not unamusing, and I had hoped that any gentleman would take a jest in better part. (*Majestically*) However, if the civil requests of your host are of no consequence to you (hiccup), let us say no more.

AUSTEN: Sir, this is not a joke. The girl's alive. I mean to find her.

TRING: Indeed? Are you interested in aeronautics, Captain Austen? Balloon ascents?

AUSTEN (*under his breath*): Cynthia, is this all a trick against me?

CYNTHIA (*also under her breath*): No, dear, of course not. (*Aloud*) I am terribly interested in balloon ascents, Mr. Tring.

TRING (*faint poison beginning to show*): "Mr. Tring"? Then it's no longer "Tommy"?

CYNTHIA (*airily*): La, sir, how can you to expect me to remember a man's Christian name from one week to the next? I am *so* forgetful.

TRING: Yes. Everyone has noticed it. But I still ask whether Captain Austen is interested in ballooning?

AUSTEN: I know something of the subject. Why?

TRING: Ah? Now that's fortunate. You see, I have persuaded Monsieur Pepotin to allow me to go up tomorrow in the car of the balloon when he makes his parachute descent. So far, I am the only passenger. I had hoped to persuade Captain Austen to accompany me.

CYNTHIA: To persuade him . . . but why?

TRING: Oh, many reasons. To state one of them: since Captain Austen has failed to find this wench of his on earth, he might amuse London still further by combing the sky for her with a spyglass.

AUSTEN (*past all endurance*): Damn your conceited soul!

CYNTHIA (*crying out*): Hugh!

THE PRINCE (*really alarmed*): Gentlemen! Gentlemen!

TRING (*agreeably*): I think you spoke, Captain Austen?

AUSTEN: I said, Damn your conceited soul. I hope that's perfectly clear. Now we know where we stand; and, if your seconds want to call on me, they'll find me at Drew's Hotel in Piccadilly.

TRING (*surprised and shocked*): Seconds? Oh, no, Captain Austen!

AUSTEN: No?

TRING: No, no, no, no! That would never do. I have other plans for such a rash lad as you. Now tell me. Er—I suppose your purse *would* run to a modest wager?

AUSTEN (*grimly*): It would.

TRING: A hundred guineas?

AUSTEN: With pleasure.

TRING: A thousand?

CYNTHIA (*under her breath*): Hugh, you know you haven't got . . . !

AUSTEN: Make it whatever you like, provided the wager suits me.

TRING: Ah, but will it suit you, Captain? *Will* it suit you? Now listen to what I propose. (*Pause*) I propose that you and I shall make the ascent in the car of the balloon tomorrow: just the two of us. I will wager a thousand guineas that only one of us reaches the ground alive. (*Carefully*) Need I add which one?

THE PRINCE (*plaintively*): Tring, I am not well; pray get me a glass of brandy.

CYNTHIA (*with cold fury*): Tommy Tring, you don't want *me*. You only want your own way.

TRING (*languidly*): Whatever I want, my dear, I mean to get it. That is my habit, and I don't propose to change it for Captain Austen or anyone else.

THE PRINCE (*deliberately*): Gentlemen—

TRING: Of course, if our gallant captain hasn't the stomach for the venture?

THE PRINCE (*with awful thunderousness*): Gentlemen, can you curb your insolent tongues for a moment in order to listen to your sovereign?

(*Dead silence.*)

TRING: My humblest apologies. Will you take snuff?

THE PRINCE: No, sir, I will not take snuff. I am vexed. I am hurt. That in my presence—my presence—you should so far forget yourself as to (*hiccup*) speak of duels—

TRING (*astonished*): Duels? But there is no question of a duel. We carry no arms. We merely go for a pleasure cruise some eight thousand feet above ground. That is, of course, if Captain Austen—?

AUSTEN: I accept the wager with pleasure.

THE PRINCE: I tell you, I won't have it! I forbid it, d'ye hear? I forbid it absolutely. As sacred guardian of my people, of their rights and duties and morals and (*breaking off reflectively*) . . . I say: won't it be a game, though?

TRING: Will three o'clock tomorrow afternoon suit your convenience, Captain Austen?

AUSTEN: Perfectly.

TRING: In Vauxhall Gardens?

AUSTEN: In Vauxhall Gardens.

TRING: Then I have the honor to wish you good night.

Your servant, sir.

AUSTEN: Yours to command, sir.

CYNTHIA (*crying out despairingly*): Oh, men! Men! Men!

EPISODE 2

NARRATOR: As the clocks are striking eleven, Captain Hugh Austen is escorting Lady Cynthia Mercer home. We see them under the great pillared porch of Carlton House, in the flare of the links, as there flows past the traffic of a hundred and thirty years ago.

(A few bars of "Auprès de ma Blonde"; then muffled street noises, carts, wheels on cobblestones, a mutter of voices.)

A LACKEY (*bellowing*): Lady Cynthia Mercer's coach!

SECOND LACKEY (*taking up the cry*): Lady Cynthia Mercer's coach!

THIRD LACKEY *(more distantly)*: Lady Cynthia Mercer's coach!

(We hear the lumbering and jingling of a heavy vehicle, which approaches and stops.)

FIRST LACKEY: Mind the step my lady. Any orders?

CYNTHIA: Tell him to drive Captain Austen to Drew's Hotel, and then take me home.

FIRST LACKEY: Very good, my lady.

(A door slams. We hear the horses' hoofs clop faintly during the following conversation.)

AUSTEN: Cynthia—

CYNTHIA (*half-sobbing*): I can't stand it, Hugh. I can't!

AUSTEN: But what could I do?

CYNTHIA: You deliberately insulted him.

AUSTEN: My dear Cynthia, didn't you notice that Tring was

determined to force a quarrel? More determined than I was? (*Thoughtfully*) I wonder why.

CYNTHIA: If I weren't so modest, perhaps *I* could tell you.

AUSTEN (*puzzled*): N-no. With all due respect to you, it was more than that. Didn't you notice his eyes? And his hands?

CYNTHIA: Fiddle-faddle!

AUSTEN: Why is he so anxious to convince everyone that I'm insane, and that the girl I met in Brussels doesn't exist? How did he come to know about that miniature?

CYNTHIA (*despairingly*): Hugh Austen, I can't understand you! Do you realize that tomorrow you're going to be *killed*? Or that poor Tommy Tring is? (*Rapidly*) It isn't as though this were an ordinary duel, though heaven knows that would be bad enough! The two of you are going up in that balloon, and one of you will be—

AUSTEN: There's something queer and unnatural about this whole night. Look out there! See the mist rising—in mid-summer. Gas and candle blurred to sparks. No sound but iron wheels on cobblestones, like the gun carriages going past that house in Brussels. There's a smell of death in the air. I haven't had this feeling since . . .

CYNTHIA (*prompting*): Since?

AUSTEN: Since the ball three nights before the battle of Waterloo, when I met that girl.

CYNTHIA (*exasperated*): Can't you *ever* stop talking about this dream of yours?

AUSTEN (*fiercely*): Cynthia, once and for all, get it out of your head that I was either mad or dreaming. Did I imagine this miniature? Did I imagine the man in black?

CYNTHIA (*startled*): The man in black? Heaven save us,

who was he? The Devil?

AUSTEN (*seriously*): I don't know. Perhaps. He was with her.

CYNTHIA (*quietly*): Hugh. Take my hand.

AUSTEN: Yes?

CYNTHIA: Now tell me about it. *All* about it.

AUSTEN: I—

CYNTHIA: Whenever you mention her, that scar on your head goes white and dreadful. I hate this girl of yours. (*Storming at him*) Yes, I do! I hate her even if she doesn't exist! But perhaps, if you told me all about it . . .

(*We hear the clop-clop of hoofs. Austen speaks in a low, absent-minded, rather intense voice.*)

AUSTEN: We were at Brussels, waiting for Boney to move. You know that. We knew Boney and the Grand Army were ahead of us, but their position wasn't certain. The Duke was waiting for news from Mons, which only reached him at midnight on the 15th. Well, that was the night of the ball.

CYNTHIA: Yes?

AUSTEN: I was an ensign then. I went with Johnny Brisbane, of the 95th Rifles, who was killed in front of La Haye Sainte. And young Greville, who fought with us at Hougoumont, and was only seventeen. Hussars, Dragoons, Highlanders: you never saw such color. I remember all the wax lights, and the smell of roses, and the sort of lilies they put on graves. I remember, when I was talking to Johnny . . .

(*The voice fades. We hear, above the mutter of a crowd, the sound of an orchestra playing a waltz. It continues to play, very faintly, through the conversation between*

Austen and Brisbane, who has a jovial, eager, young voice.)

BRISBANE (*enthusiastically*): What a night! What a night!

AUSTEN: It's infernally hot in here.

BRISBANE: That's your Guard's uniform, old boy. Now if you wore a Rifleman's green, light and comfortable . . .

AUSTEN: Also, is there any room where we are allowed to smoke?

BRISBANE (*dubiously*): Better try the garden, old boy. There may be a row if you smoke in the house— I say, the Duke's just come in!

AUSTEN: The Duke of Wellington?

BRISBANE: Old Hookey himself, and looking as though he hadn't a care in the world. (*With eager anxiety*) I say, something's certain to happen soon, isn't it? The mess is full of it. They say Boney's crossed the Sambre and given the Prussians what-for. But nobody *knows*.

AUSTEN: Which door, Johnny?

BRISBANE: Eh?

AUSTEN: The door. To the garden.

BRISBANE: Oh! Over there: that one. It leads to a passage with a line of big windows along it. You can step straight out into the garden through the windows.

(Pause.)

AUSTEN (*calling out*): This door?

BRISBANE (*more faintly*): That's it, straight through.

(A door opens slowly, and closes. The faint sound of music dies away.)

AUSTEN (*under his breath*): Long passage. . . windows . . . trees . . . moonlight . . . (*Startled*) Good Lord! I *beg* your pardon! I didn't see you sitting there in the dark.

(*The girl speaks. She has been given a start, but after an exclamation her voice is steady. She has a very sweet voice, almost sugary sweet, and it should be as much a contrast to Cynthia's as possible.*)

THE GIRL: Please don't apologize.

AUSTEN: I knocked something out of your hand, didn't I?

THE GIRL: Only an ivory miniature. Don't trouble.

AUSTEN: It's on the floor here somewhere. I'll ring for lights.

THE GIRL: Please don't. The moonlight is pleasanter. (*Vaguely*) Do you know what time it is?

AUSTEN: Past midnight, I think.

THE GIRL (*flatly*): The night is so long. (*Pause.*)

AUSTEN (*abruptly*): Forgive me. I've been admiring your beauty in the moonlight. I—

THE GIRL: Yes.

AUSTEN: I've never seen anyone lovelier.

THE GIRL: You mustn't say that.

AUSTEN: Why not? It's true. (*Breaking off*) You're shivering. Aren't you afraid of taking cold in the night air?

THE GIRL: No. It is much colder where I come from.

AUSTEN (*sharply*): I don't understand

THE GIRL: I come from . . . a long distance away. And all for nothing. What they say is true, isn't it? The Prince *isn't* in Brussels?

AUSTEN (*grimly*): What particular prince, among our galaxy?

THE GIRL: The Prince Regent of England.

AUSTEN (*astonished*): Of England? Good Lord, no! *He* wouldn't be with the army.

THE GIRL: It was a foolish notion, I know. In the story books, you see, anyone who is in trouble and can't find any other way out always goes to the king. And he listens to her. But I wouldn't go to our king, because they say he's old and mad and blind, poor man. So I thought that perhaps the Prince . . . this wonderful person I've heard so much about ever since I was a little girl . . . . But that's only in the story books. Oh, God, I was a fool!

AUSTEN: You're in trouble?

THE GIRL: Yes. They say I did . . . something dreadful.

AUSTEN (*quietly*): Go on.

THE GIRL: Please. You wouldn't understand.

AUSTEN: Possibly. Many things puzzle me in this world, but I think that, whatever it was you told me, I should understand.

THE GIRL (*wonderingly*): I believe you mean that.

AUSTEN: Mean it? I—

THE GIRL: Wait! Now see how the spell will be broken. Here comes a servant with a taper to light the candles.

AUSTEN (*calling*): Hoy! There! Must you light the candles?

A SERVANT: Monsieur?

AUSTEN: Est-ce qu'il faut allumer les chandelles?

THE SERVANT (*expostulatingly*): Mais, monsieur! On passe par ici à la salle-à-manger!

AUSTEN (*to the girl*): This appears to be the way through to the supper room. They'll be coming in presently. (*To the servant*) Bien. Continuez. (*To the girl, fascinated*) Besides, I wanted to see you in the light. Your hair *is* golden. And your eyes are gray, but they change. No, don't look down.

THE GIRL (*sharply*): Listen!

AUSTEN: What is it?

THE GIRL: Didn't you hear a bugle?

AUSTEN: No, I heard nothing.

(*A door opens and closes sharply.*)

BRISBANE (*calling from a distance*): Hugh! I say, Hugh!

THE GIRL (*terrified*): Who's that?

AUSTEN: Only Johnny Brisbane, a friend of mine.

THE GIRL: He mustn't see me. Nobody must see me.

BRISBANE (*panting with excitement*): Hugh, it's Boney! So help me, it's Boney!

AUSTEN: Well?

BRISBANE: Listen! The Duke knew all about it tonight, but he came to the ball just the same, to keep people quiet. He says there's no hurry. He says to go on with the dancing and not interrupt supper—

AUSTEN: O England!

BRISBANE: —but here are our orders. We're not to do any more drinking. We're to slip away, one by one, and join our companies, so that nobody notices us go. (*Significantly*) Won't they notice it, though!

AUSTEN (*fiercely*): But what about Boney?

BRISBANE (*gabbling*): He's on top of us, that's what! He's driven back the Prussians and taken Charleroi, and his left wing is moving up ahead to cut us off. (*Ecstatically*) By gad, we'll see Boney's fat face at last!

(*Faintly and distantly a bugle sounds the "Assembly" and repeats it. A drum begins to tap.*)

BRISBANE (*in consternation*): I say, I hope I didn't drive the lady away.

AUSTEN (*shouting at him*): Where is she?

BRISBANE: She slipped out into the garden, old boy. See

here: what's this on the floor?

AUSTEN: It's a miniature. Give it to me.

BRISBANE: Here you are. Now I've got to run. You follow her. And good luck.

AUSTEN: Good luck.

(*The door opens and closes. The ruffle of drums grows louder, dies, and then is followed by a vast mutter. Then we hear a new voice speak. It is a very deep, slow, distinctive voice, which suggests a heavy man about fifty.*)

THE VOICE: Ensign Austen?

AUSTEN (*startled*): What the Devil—

THE VOICE (*as though summoning*): Ensign . . . Austen.

AUSTEN: Did someone call me?

THE VOICE: *I* called you, sir. You will pardon me for remaining outside the window until your friend had gone. You don't know me, but I should like a word with you.

AUSTEN: I'm afraid I can't wait. I'm looking . . .

THE VOICE: You are looking, I think, for the lady who left you a moment ago.

AUSTEN (*pulled up short*): Yes! (*Tentatively*) Her name is . . . ?

THE VOICE: I trust you will not misunderstand if I say that her name can convey nothing to you. And you need not trouble to search for the lady any longer. She has gone.

AUSTEN: Gone!

THE VOICE (*still without emotion*): One further word. You hear the noises out there? Gun carriages and still more gun carriages. (*Judicially*) It is probable that within a few hours you will be dead. However, you may survive. Some do, even in a Europe so blackened with powder as this. If so, you will be good enough to forget that you have ever seen the lady.

AUSTEN: May I ask, sir, just who the Devil you are?

THE VOICE: My name does not matter. I am, in a sense, the lady's guardian.

AUSTEN: Guardian?

THE VOICE: In a sense. I wear black, you observe. Now, young man, will you heed what I say? (*With terrifying heaviness*) If not, I warn you . . .

AUSTEN: Against what?

THE VOICE: Against worse things than you are likely to see on the battlefield.

AUSTEN: The man's raving mad. Let me pass!

THE VOICE: As you like.

(*Again the bugle sounds and repeats "Assembly." The rumbling as of iron wheels thickens and deepens. The door opens and closes.*)

BRISBANE: Hugh, I say! Wait!

AUSTEN (*wildly*): Lord in heaven, are you back again?

BRISBANE (*hurt*): I offered to come and fetch you, old boy. It's Colonel MacDonnell. He's in a real hieland rage. The guards are moving on Quatre Bras before daylight. If you don't join your company at once, he'll have you court-martialled.

AUSTEN: But the Duke himself said there was no hurry! Just five minutes, Johnny. Five minutes. I was only talking to the Gentleman . . .

BRISBANE: What gentleman?

AUSTEN (*dazed*): Eh?

BRISBANE: I said, what gentleman, old boy. There's no-body here but us two.

(*The rolling of the gun carriages deepens. It is taken up*

by the drums and then by a band which strikes up "The British Grenadiers." This presently dies away and fades into the clop-clop of horses' hoofs. Austen speaks, his voice now hard and bitter.)

AUSTEN: —and that's all I can tell you about it, Cynthia. Three days later we met Boney at Waterloo. I was hit rather badly, and they kept me in bed for months.

CYNTHIA: Yes. Poor Hugh!

AUSTEN (*peevishly*): Why "Poor Hugh"?

CYNTHIA (*softly*): Do you remember much about the battle?

AUSTEN: Not much. We held Hougoumont. They were over the wall like rats. There was fire . . .

CYNTHIA (*with affectionate derision*): Twice mentioned for bravery and doesn't remember it! (*Quietly*) Even as you tell me about it, don't you *see* it was a dream?

AUSTEN (*abruptly; suddenly in despair*): I don't know.

CYNTHIA: The mysterious girl who doesn't like light and carries a miniature of *herself.* The even more mysterious "man in black" who appears and disappears at will, so that even poor Johnny Brisbane never saw him. Oh, Hugh, is it likely such things ever happened? Didn't you pick up the miniature somewhere, and then, when you were ill and delirious, you imagined . . .?

AUSTEN: Don't say that, Cynthia.

CYNTHIA: Can't you face the truth?

AUSTEN: No.

CYNTHIA (*derisively*): Fiddle-faddle! A girl you saw for perhaps five minutes!

AUSTEN: There it is.

CYNTHIA: What makes me positively boil with anger is that it's all so unnecessary. Because of this dream, you'll insult anyone who doubts it. Because of this dream, you and Tommy Tring are going to try to kill each other tomorrow . . .

AUSTEN: Yes.

CYNTHIA: It's most unjust and inconsiderate. I declare, I'm beginning to think you were not even *at* the Duchess of Richmond's ball. (*Reflecting*) Did you see Tommy Tring there, for instance?

AUSTEN (*astonished*): Tring was there that night?

CYNTHIA (*also surprised*): La, but of course he was! He was traveling abroad at the time, and said the women were *most* interesting.

AUSTEN (*under his breath*): I knew it!

CYNTHIA (*crossly*): You knew what? . . . Now kindly don't sit there in that ridiculous way, pounding your fist on your knee! What is it?

AUSTEN: Tring knows I'm not dreaming.

CYNTHIA: Oh?

AUSTEN (*as though groping at a problem*): I repeat: why is Tring so infernally anxious to discredit me? I tell you, I was watching that rather-too-handsome phiz of his. Granted that I've got a bee in my bonnet: why has he got one in his?

CYNTHIA: Well why?

AUSTEN: Tomorrow, when we are about eight or ten thousand feet up in the clouds, I am going to try to find out. And I remember many things. For instance, twice in the past week there's been a sneak thief in my hotel room. Why?

CYNTHIA: Oh, hotels!

AUSTEN: But the thief didn't take anything. I never thought

about it at the time. All the same—

CYNTHIA (*blazing at him*): Oh, go on with your silly wager! (*Bitterly*) You'll enjoy it, I suppose?

AUSTEN (*seriously*): No. The man who says he enjoys the prospect of dying is either a fool or a liar. (*Hesitating*) To tell you the truth, I haven't a good head for heights. I discovered that when we were experimenting with observation balloons for the army.

CYNTHIA: Then? (*No reply.*) (*Impatiently*) I said, then?

AUSTEN: Tomorrow.

EPISODE 3

NARRATOR: In old Vauxhall Gardens, by the bandstand among the gravel walks, there is today a new spectacle. The great balloon is already inflated and tugging at its mooring ropes. Its oiled silk surface, painted in gaudy stripes of red and yellow, seems to loom as huge as the dome of St. Paul's over the trees and the crowd. It is moored high up, since beneath its car there hangs the parachute by which Monsieur Pepotin will make his descent. Imagine a canvas umbrella some twenty-five feet in diameter with ropes at its edges supporting a basket underneath for Monsieur Pepotin to stand in, and you will see the parachute of the year eighteen hundred and sixteen.

The band has been playing at full blast. Horse, foot, and wagon, a dense crowd has gathered to bask in the sunshine and drink rack punch. Leaning out of a gig, their tall hats awry, are three dandies from St. James, come to see the sport.

(*We hear the shifting and mutter and laughter of a crowd, then voices.*)

FIRST DANDY: Damme, if that balloon don't seem alive. Listen to her creak.

SECOND DANDY (*languidly*): Frankly, my boy, I wouldn't care to stand in the Frenchman's shoes now.

FIRST DANDY: Nor I. He'll come down wallop. Just you

wait.

SECOND DANDY: Hardly as bad as that, old boy.

FIRST DANDY (*challengingly*): No? Three to one he's killed!

SECOND DANDY: Unsportsmanlike, old boy. Even money he ain't killed but breaks a leg.

FIRST DANDY: Make it two legs and I'm your man.

SECOND DANDY: Done!

FIRST DANDY: Twenty guineas?

SECOND DANDY: Done!

THIRD DANDY (*pettishly*): Be quiet, you two! Who cares a farthing what happens to the Frenchman? What we want to know is what happens to the wager between Tommy Tring and Captain Austen.

SECOND DANDY (*blankly*): Wager, old boy?

THIRD DANDY: Strike me blind, is it possible you haven't heard? You *haven't*?

BOTH TOGETHER: No.

THIRD DANDY (*greedily*): Austen is the lunatic who thinks he met a gel in Brussels and fell in love with her. Only he didn't; he got a knock on the head at Waterloo and dreamed it. Don't you remember? —We saw him at Carlton House with Lady Cynthia Mercer.

FIRST DANDY: Yes, but—

THIRD DANDY: Tring made sport of Austen, and Austen didn't like it. The fur flew, I can tell you. Then Tommy challenged Austen to go up in the car of Pepotin's balloon and bet him he wouldn't come down alive.

FIRST DANDY (*with a whistle*): No joke?

THIRD DANDY: No joke!

SECOND DANDY: I say, does Pepotin know about this?

THIRD DANDY: No; that's half the sport. The Frenchman wouldn't want his thunder stolen, would he? Either Tring or Austen is going to come down a devilishly sight faster than *he* does.

(*A roar and a burst of cheering deepens across the gardens.*)

SECOND DANDY (*galvanized*): Look!

FIRST DANDY: Where?

THIRD DANDY: In the open carriage with the four bays! It's Prinny himself. And Alvanley! And Poodle Byng! And Kangaroo Cooke! And Dan Mackinnon! (*Ecstatically*) Half of St. James's is here.

SECOND DANDY: All the crackpots, you mean.

THIRD DANDY: There they come! There's Tommy Tring in the bottle-green coat and white hat. That's Captain Austen behind him. And there's Pepotin . . . the little monkey-like fellow . . . running out to meet 'em.

(*The noise of the crowd grows, with some laughter, and then dies. Pepotin speaks. He has a quick, shrill, and clear-cut voice.*)

PEPOTIN (*urgently*): Monsieur Tring!

TRING (*with smiling condescension*): Good afternoon, Pepotin. Everything is ready for us, I hope?

PEPOTIN (*worried*): Monsieur Tring, I do not understand.

TRING: No?

PEPOTIN: Last night you have write me a note to say you will bring along another gentleman to ride with you in the car of my balloon.

TRING: You don't mind?

PEPOTIN: No, no, no! It is not that. No: I think that the more weight we have, the better. (*Sinking his voice con-*

fidentially) But, monsieur, I am worried. This balloon—I do not like the way she behave.

TRING: It does seem to be rather tugging at the bit. Is that good or bad?

PEPOTIN: Sh-h! Monsieur Tring, I tell you a little secret. This balloon, she is filled with coal gas. I pipe him from the gas main that light these Gardens. Listen! (*Rapidly and urgently*) This hydrogen they use, she is expensive to make and she take all day to fill the bag. With coal gas, she fill in an hour and she go up—whish! (*Anxiously*) You do not mind?

TRING: My good Pepotin, *I* don't mind what you use. But Captain Austen here seems to find something amusing in it. Don't you, Austen?

AUSTEN: Yes. You might tell your friends who are smoking cigars that if a spark touches that balloon the result will be extremely unpleasant.

TRING (*coolly*): Oh? It's dangerous stuff, then?

PEPOTIN (*deprecatingly*): A very little, monsieur! —You are perhaps an aeronaut, Captain Austen?

AUSTEN: I've been up a number of times, yes.

PEPOTIN (*relieved*): Ah? You perhaps know how to handle a valve line?

AUSTEN: Pretty well.

PEPOTIN: Ah? Can you make a record of our height from the barometer?

AUSTEN: I think so.

PEPOTIN: That is good. I have tried to teach Monsieur Tring, but I am not always sure if he understand. What do you think of my notion to use the coal gas?

AUSTEN: The notion of coal gas, Monsieur Pepotin, is

brilliant. So far as I know, it has never been used before.

PEPOTIN (*breathing proudly*): Haah! —you see!

AUSTEN: But in this case, frankly, I do not care for it.

PEPOTIN (*anguished*): But, monsieur—!

AUSTEN: This parachute of yours, with your own weight added, will weigh over three hundred pounds. Have you calculated what will happen to the balloon when you release the parachute and suddenly take the weight away from it?

PEPOTIN: Well! Perhaps the balloon will roll a bit: yes. Perhaps she will start to rise up damn-quick. But all you have to do is pull on the valve line. That will let some of the gas out, and down she go all steady again. This noble balloon has two escape valves, one at the top and one at the bottom.

AUSTEN: But you still don't see—

PEPOTIN: Monsieur, you are making me mad. Who is going to risk his life in that parachute? You or me? I make perhaps a martyr of myself, and all you can do is ask what will happen to you. (*With hollow and offended rage*) Ah, mon dieu, no! That is too much.

KANGAROO COOKE (*shouting from the background*): Ahoy there! Tring!

TRING: Yes?

COOKE: I have a message from the Prince: His Highness is graciously pleased to ask what the Devil is delaying you.

PEPOTIN: We are desolated to have upset His Highness! We are ready! We go at once!

COOKE: There's a brute of a wind blowing up from the river. Hold tight to the car.

PEPOTIN: You are ready, messieurs?

TRING: Yes.

AUSTEN: Yes.

PEPOTIN (*warningly*): You have greatcoats and gloves? It will be very cold up there . . . Good! Then climb up the rope ladder to the car, and pull it up when you are there.

TRING: After you, Captain Austen.

AUSTEN (*ironically polite*): After *you*, Mr. Tring.

TRING: As you like.

PEPOTIN: My instruments are in the car. Use them. You shall keep shouting to me how high up we are. When I am ready I shall pull the catch to release me, and God help all . . . You!

A HOARSE VOICE: Yes, guv'nor?

PEPOTIN: You shall help me into this basket. Then tell the bandmaster to give us a roll of drums.

THE VOICE (*urgently*): You'd better hurry up and give the word to cast off, guv'nor. These stakes won't hold her down much longer.

PEPOTIN: I tell you it is all right. I admit my heart go hammer-bump a bit, but I make history. You see . . . (*Calling*) Ready aloft?

TRING (*to Austen*): This car could be larger, cleaner, and more comfortable.

AUSTEN: Never mind how clean it is. I don't like the way that gas bag bulges down nearly on our necks.

TRING: Really?

AUSTEN: I shouldn't try to move about, Tring. Take off your hat, sit down, and hold to the rim of the car.

TRING (*languidly interested*): And this rope, I believe, is the valve line?

AUSTEN: It is.

TRING: If we find ourselves going too high, we pull this line, which lets some of the gas out of the valve, and down we go.

AUSTEN: Correct again.

TRING: But what, my friend, is all this corded rubble and metal on the floor? There's hardly room to move our feet. Can't we chuck it overboard and give ourselves more room?

AUSTEN: Let it alone! If you want to throw the grappling hook overboard before we start, our little argument will begin here and now. What's the matter with you? Haven't you ever been up before?

TRING (*as though grinning*): Merely light conversation to beguile the tedious minutes. But you don't seem to find them tedious, Captain Austen. In fact, I should say you were looking a bit green round the gills.

AUSTEN: Am I?

TRING (*amused still more*): Don't deny it. An impolite person would say you were in a fit of the blue shivers.

AUSTEN: Maybe I realize a little better than you do what is likely to happen to us.

TRING: Oh? And what is likely to happen to us?

AUSTEN: You'll find out soon enough.

TRING: Green gills and blue shivers. Not an attractive combination, either for a coat or a face. If our Cynthia could see you now, she might not be so proud of her gallant fire-eater. Speaking personally, I am enjoying myself.

AUSTEN: You might wait until that parachute is released and see whether you enjoy yourself then.

TRING: I have every intention of—

AUSTEN (*irascibly*): Be quiet, can't you?

TRING (*musingly*): Nervous as tortoise-shell cat. Adding still another color to our list. There is still time to cry off the wager, you know. Though I shouldn't care to climb down in either sense with all those people watching.

AUSTEN: Be quiet, will you? Pepotin's trying to attract our attention down there. I can't hear a word he's saying. (*As though making a trumpet of his hands and shouting*) Yes? What is it?

PEPOTIN (*his voice coming from some distance*): Away! Ready aloft?

AUSTEN: Ready!

PEPOTIN: Reading?

AUSTEN: Time, three-fourteen. Temperature, fifty-nine. Dewpoint, fifty.

PEPOTIN: Prepare to cast off! (*A long, steady roll of drums rises and deepens.*) Cast off!
(*Whatever noises may be made by the balloon are drowned in the din of a march played by the band. This continues for some seconds and dies away. We hear the noise of the wind: a steady, whistling whine.*)

PEPOTIN: Height?

AUSTEN: Two thousand feet.

TRING (*languidly*): We're going up rather fast, aren't we?

AUSTEN: Yes.

TRING: And must we swing round and round like this? It's like a blasted teetotum. If I hadn't a head for heights, I should be completely dizzy now.

AUSTEN (*through his teeth*): Yes.

TRING (*cheerfully*): But then I have a head for heights. Have you, my friend? Cynthia Mercer says you haven't. (*No reply*) Look down there. Like a living map, isn't it?

Clear, cold sun up here; soot clouds down there. I never realized what an infernally dirty town we live in. (*More interested*) It's a curious sensation. Light—as though I had wings. I feel as though I might almost be able to fly myself.

AUSTEN (*grimly*): Don't try it.

TRING: What height does the old boy intend to jump from?

AUSTEN: I don't know. He'll give us the word.

TRING: A settlement of our more personal affairs, my friend, can wait for a while. It should be as high up as possible . . . And this, it appears, is a cloud bank. A magnificent sight!

AUSTEN: Heights seem to make you talkative. I didn't know you could exert yourself to talk.

TRING: There are many things about me that you don't know.

AUSTEN: I daresay.

TRING (*amused*): Now is that, I wonder, intended to trap me into being indiscreet? You would dearly love to make me indiscreet, wouldn't you? So many people would.

AUSTEN: But they never do?

TRING: Why should they? Why give them that satisfaction? To Prinny I am an authority on cravats and horseflesh. To my Aunt Henrietta I am . . . oh, such a long-headed fellow! (*Laughs*) To Cynthia I am all heat and sighs, like a furnace . . .

AUSTEN: Yes.

TRING: I even have my serious side. I go gravely to the Royal Society and experiment with opium on animals, and the science of aeronautics. And up here I am a poet. Now you, for instance; I should never have given you credit for the imagination to invent that girl—the one you say you met at Brussels.

AUSTEN: That's one of the things we have to discuss, isn't it?

TRING: Yes.

(*A pause while the whistling of the wind grows more shrill.*)

PEPOTIN: Height?

AUSTEN: Six thousand, eight hundred feet.

PEPOTIN (*as though half strangled*): I think I must jump soon.

AUSTEN (*fiercely*): Not yet! Give yourself more height!

PEPOTIN: But if this go on I shall freeze.

TRING: He's right there. My face and fingers are numb, and my head feels uncommonly odd. Perhaps—

AUSTEN (*sharply*): What have you got there?

TRING: This? A piece of lighted candle carefully shielded in a dark-lantern.

AUSTEN: Lighted candle! You don't propose to smoke a cigar up here?

TRING: As a matter of fact, I brought it along to keep me warm. (*Reflecting*) But come to think of it, if I could manage to light a cigar—

AUSTEN: Do you want to blow us all to pieces? Put it out!

TRING (*coolly*): Better stay where you are, my friend. You might look at what I've got in my other hand.

AUSTEN: So you brought a pistol, eh?

TRING (*surprised*): Naturally.

AUSTEN: Well?

TRING: Now that the fences are down, perhaps we can understand each other. I don't mean to use it; that is, if you behave. Cynthia supplied me with another plan for you. I'm going to watch you die, Austen. I intend to let your imagination, which can't endure heights, finish the work for me. Here we are now, slung on a cobweb and still rising. I intend to watch you growing whiter and whiter . . . look at you now . . . as your legs weaken at the knees . . .

(*Shrill sound of wind.*)

PEPOTIN: Height?

TRING: . . . and you feel you can't endure the altitude any longer . . .

PEPOTIN (*screaming*): Height?

AUSTEN (*breathing hard*): Nine thousand . . . four hundred feet.

PEPOTIN: Crouch down in the car. I am going to count three and then jump.

AUSTEN: Tring, for God's sake blow out that candle!

TRING: Stay where you are.

AUSTEN: Do you know what's going to happen?

PEPOTIN (*crying out*): Jesu! Mary! Aid me!

AUSTEN: Listen to me There he g. . . LOOK OUT!
      (*Two heavy thumps. The whine of the wind changes to a tumultuous roar.*)

TRING (*faintly fearful for the first time, but game*): Austen!

AUSTEN (*grimly*): Yes?

TRING: What happened? (*Gasping*) What is happening?

AUSTEN: What happened is that you nearly went overboard. Your dark-lantern did go overboard.

TRING: We started to turn upside down.

AUSTEN: We very nearly did, and we're still doing it. She's going to roll again. Hold very tight unless you want your cobweb to drop you. Listen to me, now. Can you reach the valve line?

TRING: No.

AUSTEN: Try.

TRING: I can't; we're spinning too much. And my fingers are numb. And there's a devilish odd pain in my ears like someone pushing knitting needles into my head . . .

AUSTEN: You'll feel it worse unless you reach that valve line. Try! I can't see or I—

TRING: Got it!

AUSTEN: Good. Now pull. Gently at first.

(*There is a hissing noise of gas escaping.*)

TRING: We're still rising.

AUSTEN: Pull! Harder!

(*The hissing increases.*)

TRING: We're still rising, but we're steadier. The car's level again. (*Recovering himself a little, with some jauntiness*) Now I should call that a most perilous close shave. (*Pause, and then abruptly*) I say, Austen. What's that smell? Rum stuff to breathe. It gets into your nostrils. It— (*begins to cough*)

AUSTEN: That, my friend, is coal gas.

TRING: Coal gas?

AUSTEN: Pouring straight down into our faces from the escape valve. We're rising so fast that the upper valve is blocked by the air pressure, so it's pouring out from the lower valve.

TRING (*coughing*): But we'll suffocate!

AUSTEN (*also coughing*): Exactly.

TRING: We could—

AUSTEN: Oh, yes. You can close the valve and die from

lack of air in your lungs as we go on up. Five, six, seven miles. (*Pauses, gasping*) I warned you and Pepotin. But you . . . (*His voice grows weaker.*) You . . .

TRING: Stand up, man! Stand up!

AUSTEN: I said— (*The gas hisses.*)

TRING: I can't hear you. It's all banging and roaring in my ears. I . . . I'm not afraid to die, but . . . Devil take me if I die . . . like this.

AUSTEN (*dimly*): What did you say?

TRING: I've still got my pistol. I'll put a ball through the gas bag and we'll go to glory like gentlemen. Be ready when I count three. One . . . (*more faintly*) . . . two . . .
(*The voice weakens. We hear the loud hissing of gas.*)

EPISODE 4

NARRATOR: So presently the darkness fell. And the yellow moon rose across flat and marshy lands, breathing with mist. Nobody saw the great balloon drift down, the oiled silk bag flattened, its netting tangled, its car bumping the tree tops. No grappling hook searched the ground. Nothing stirred inside. Nobody saw the envelope spread itself across the trees of a coppice, the car jerking and swinging within a foot or two of earth.

It had long since ceased to swing. In the car two men lay huddled and motionless. One had an arm out as though to seize. The other was still gripping an unfired pistol in one hand, and the other hand was twisted round the valve line of the balloon. But both were breathing faintly. It was the first man who stirred . . .

AUSTEN (*faintly and weakly*): Don't fire, you fool! . . . Don't . . . (*Pause*) We're not moving . . . (*Pause*) Tring! (*More loudly*) Tring! (*Pause*) (*Wonderingly*) I'm not dead, I suppose. But I might be. They say . . . No, I'm too sick to be dead: joke . . . Tring! (*A hump and stir as of someone stumbling on wood*) If I can climb down from here . . . No dizziness, now. Steady does it. Steady, and jump . . . (*A thud*) (*Still to himself in a ghostly whisper*) No, don't fall over. Stand up. Never mind if you feel sick: stand up. Black trees. Swampy ground. I might be dead and in hell. Tring's dead. Or is he? . . . Must find

a doctor . . . Must find . . . someone . . . (*Calling*) Hallo!
Hallo! Hallo!

A VOICE (*faintly*): Did someone call?

AUSTEN: Here! . . . Help! . . .

(*The voice talks through its nose, faintly and importantly.
It suggests a thin little man in his middle fifties.*)

THE VOICE (*cajoling*): Whoa, Dobbin! Nice brute. Let me
down. I most distinctly heard . . . (*Breaking off*) Good
gad!

AUSTEN: It's all right.

THE VOICE: You will allow me to suggest, sir, that it is distinctly not right. How did you come here?

AUSTEN: In a balloon.

THE VOICE: A most improbable assertion, sir. I am a man
of the law, accustomed to dealing with testimony. Permit
me: Godfrey is my name, Elias Godfrey.

AUSTEN (*ironically amused*): Er—how do you do?

GODFREY (*briskly*): However, we have no time for the
civilities now. I have a flask of brandy in my saddle-bag.
If you will come with me . . .

AUSTEN: My friend . . .

GODFREY: There's another of you, then?

AUSTEN: In the car of the balloon. He—he may be dead.

GODFREY: (*Clucks his tongue.*)

AUSTEN: Can you tell me where we are?

GODFREY (*with a shade of apology*): That, sir, is something I wish I knew myself.

AUSTEN: You don't know?

GODFREY (*coughing and hemming*): The fact is, I am on
circuit. I had stopped at the Bell Inn at Chatterham,
where I . . . ah . . . fell in with a group of legal cronies.

We sat down to yarn over a pipe and punch bowl. One punch bowl begat two. I somewhat hazily remember being propped on a horse . . .

AUSTEN (*desperately*): If you would kindly—!

GODFREY: . . . and the horse told to go home. That was some hours ago, I fancy. But since it did not happen to be *my* horse, I have no notion towards whose home I may be proceeding. Allow me to adjust my spectacles. (*In a different tone*) Good gad! You're telling the truth. It is a balloon!

AUSTEN (*groaning*): Of course it is! Don't you understand? He may be dying . . .

GODFREY (*competently*): I will see to him. Do you feel strong enough to walk?

AUSTEN: I think so.

GODFREY: Good. About a hundred yards back along the road I observed a house. A most sinister looking house, suggesting panelled rooms and ghosts. Still, a house. I had considered calling there myself, except that I have a rooted objection to dogs chewing my legs. Knock them up and ask for sanctuary. I will see to your friend.

AUSTEN: Which way?

GODFREY: Straight on. H'm. At least, you do not appear to have been molested. There are no footprints in this marsh but your own. When did you land?

AUSTEN: I—I don't know. We left London at past three o'clock . . .

GODFREY (*amazed*): London! You are now somewhere in the middle of Suffolk, I think. But get on with you; that is, if you can make it.

AUSTEN (*gritting his teeth*): I can make it. (*A long pause, and then the sound of squelching footsteps*) (*Muttering to himself*) He's right. It's an evil-looking house. Something foreign about it, too. I might almost be back in Brussels . . . Lamp in the side window . . . and it sounds . . . like someone . . . playing a spinet . . .

(*His voice trails away. We hear the wiry tinkle of a spinet playing the first few bars of "Auprès de ma Blonde," and a girl's voice humming.*)

THE GIRL (*singing to the tune, very softly*):
Au jardin de mon père,
    Les lauriers sont fleuris;
Au jardin de mon père,
    Les lauriers sont fleuris . . .

AUSTEN: I *am* dead or mad. It's . . .

THE GIRL (*singing, still softly*):
Au service du roi
    Il me faudra partir . . .
Auprès de ma blonde
    Qu'il fait bon, fait bon, fait bon,
Auprès de ma blonde
    Qu'il fait bon dormir!

AUSTEN: If I can get this window open . . .

THE GIRL (*startled*): Oh!

AUSTEN: Don't be alarmed. (*Pause*) You won't remember me. But I met you just a year ago last night in Brussels. (*Doubtfully*) You're real, aren't you? You *are* real?

THE GIRL: Don't I seem real? As real as I did that night?

AUSTEN (*quickly, a statement rather than a question*): Then you do remember me.

THE GIRL: Of course.

AUSTEN: You see, I want to make sure I'm not imagining

this. Everybody in London says I dreamed you. They say you don't exist. —May I climb in through the window?

THE GIRL (*hesitates*): Yes, but (*urgently and softly*) please don't make any noise. . . Oh!

AUSTEN: Admittedly, I am not looking my best. There was an accident. We came down in a balloon . . .

THE GIRL: That scar across your forehead! You didn't have that when . . .

AUSTEN: No. That's a relic of the battle of Waterloo. Also, it's one of the reasons why they say I'm out of my head. But I'm not out of my head, unless this house, and the spinet, and the lamp, and the fire, and the yellow satin are all a piece of fantasy too. Before anything else, tell me your name. If I knew your name, I should have something to hold to.

THE GIRL (*after a hesitation*): My name is Mary.

AUSTEN (*insistently*): Mary what?

MARY: Mary . . . Adair.

AUSTEN (*savoring it*): Mary Adair. May I look at you? (*Pause*) You're paler, I think. And you wear your hair differently. But that white dress becomes you as much as . . . Mary Adair, there's something I must tell you now, or I may not have the courage to say it. I'm in love with you. No, don't shrink away. I've been in love with you ever since that night in Brussels. Do you remember the long gallery? And the garden?

MARY: Whatever I remember, I mustn't think of it. And neither must you. Please believe that!

AUSTEN (*unheeding, with fierce jubilation*): And they said I was mad! They almost made me believe it myself! But tell me everything. Where are we? Whose house is this?

Yours?

MARY (*troubled*): No.

AUSTEN: Then—

MARY (*in a lower voice*): It's Dr. Cameron's house.

AUSTEN: Dr. Cameron?

MARY: You . . . I think you met him . . . that night. A big, thick-set elderly man, with old fashioned hair powder; dressed all in black.

AUSTEN (*exultantly*): The man in black! So he's real too! And Cynthia said *he* was only a nightmare!

MARY (*rather sharply*): Cynthia?

AUSTEN: A lady who, with the best intentions in the world, nearly finished me. (*Exalted*) Oh, Mary, Mary, quite contrary!

MARY (*quietly*): Didn't Dr. Cameron warn you?

AUSTEN (*brought up short*): I beg your pardon?

MARY (*flatly*): He told you—about me.

AUSTEN: No! That's just it!

MARY: He didn't say *anything*?

AUSTEN: Not a word, except some nonsense I couldn't understand.

MARY (*still more troubled*): You see, he saw you talking to me. And he didn't like it. Oh, not for the reason you might think! He's old enough to be my father.

AUSTEN: He said he was your guardian.

MARY (*quickly*): Yes! That's it! My guardian—at a time when I was ill and beaten and helpless, and needed a guardian if ever anybody did. He's been wonderful to me. But when he saw us talking at the ball, he knew we *mustn't* see each other again. So he found out who you were . . . (*As though studying him*) Your name is Hugh, isn't it? Hugh Austen?

AUSTEN: Yes.

MARY: That was why he warned you away. I never thought
I should see you again.

AUSTEN (*astonished*): You didn't by any chance want to see
me again?

MARY (*after a pause*): Yes.

AUSTEN (*still more astonished*): And you didn't think I
would be warned away?

MARY (*quickly*): Weren't you? You haven't been . . . ?

AUSTEN: Searching for you? Every minute. Every bitter
minute since then.

MARY: You poor, dear *fool*.

AUSTEN (*wryly*): Thanks. That's the most lenient description I've heard in three hundred and sixty-five days.
Mary, my dear, I am known as a dangerous maniac,
merely for the lunacy of saying you existed. Never mind.
That doesn't matter now.

MARY: Oh, but it does matter! It matters very much. If
only I could tell you the truth! If only I could!

AUSTEN: Well, is there any reason in this world why you
can't?

MARY: Yes. If you knew the truth, you wouldn't want me.

AUSTEN: (*Laughs*)

MARY: It's true. You would believe what all those others
believed, all those people who came to see me . . .
(*Her voice trails away.*)

AUSTEN: I didn't quite hear what you said. To see—what?

MARY (*as though trying to change the subject yet unable to
get away from it*): And there are other reasons too.
Reasons that are horrible, and yet real. I've sometimes

wondered whether anyone, *anyone*, has ever been in quite the position I'm in. You say nobody would believe I existed. Why wouldn't anyone believe it?

AUSTEN: Because they thought I was mad. They said I had imagined you, or . . .

MARY (*quickly, with insistent prompting*): Or what?

AUSTEN (*uncomfortable without knowing why*): Or that you weren't the real flesh and blood you obviously are. Give me your hand.

MARY: No. It's better not.

AUSTEN (*bitterly*): I mayn't even have your hand, then?

MARY: If I give you my hand, I might be tempted to give you my heart and soul and body as well. And that can't be, Hugh Austen, for such as *I* am.

AUSTEN (*cheerfully unimpressed*): And what *are* you, Mary-quite-contrary?

MARY (*miserably*): I don't know.

AUSTEN: Nonsense!

MARY: It's perfectly true.

AUSTEN: Where are you going?

MARY: Only to the spinet. Come here, where we can see each other in the light. You see this song on the music rack?

AUSTEN: Yes.

MARY: It's a new song by Mr. Moore. Will you read the words?

AUSTEN (*puzzled but reading aloud*): "Believe me, if all those endearing young charms, which I gazed on so fondly today, were to fade by tomorrow . . ." (*He breaks off, suddenly realizing.*) (*Grimly*) I think I can take a hint. Are you—shall we say—letting the poor devil down lightly? Is this your polite manner of saying you don't wish to see me again?

MARY (*after a pause*): I meant it to be. (*Another pause*) But I can't. God help both of us, I can't!

AUSTEN: Wait! Stop! I didn't mean to hurt you.

MARY: You haven't hurt me—except by just existing. And being there. And searching for me all this time.

AUSTEN: Mary, what *is* all this mystery? Why can't you speak out?

MARY (*slowly*): Yes. You deserve to know. Besides— sooner or later you'll only hear it from others. The very mountebanks I used to live with can tell you all about Mary Adair, though I don't think they realized, even at the end, how well they had taught her. If I tell you, will you promise not to look at me while I do? Will you promise not to go away afterwards?

AUSTEN (*fervently*): Go away afterwards? My dear, if you promise *me* that, why should you tell me anything? Why should you distress yourself.

MARY: I don't mind now. That's all a part of—another life.

AUSTEN: If I can be with you, and see you, and talk to you, I don't give a hang . . . (*A chord on the spinet is struck sharply, as though uncontrollably.*) I don't give a hang what this mysterious story may be.

MARY: Are you quite sure of that? Can you look me in the eyes and say you're not afraid of me?

AUSTEN (*amused*): Afraid of *you*?

MARY (*seriously*): Yes. There might be things to be frightened of, even about me. Many people were frightened of me, once; even a man who pleaded for me. Are you so sure of what you feel, Hugh Austen?

AUSTEN: Quite sure. All I know or care is that I've found you. What does it matter? Let me look at you again! I feel like dancing the highland fling. Gad, I'll even apologize to— (*Stops abruptly*) Tring. I forgot Tring.

MARY: Who is he?

AUSTEN: A fellow I made a foolish wager with. We . . . well, we've had some adventures. He's hurt.

MARY: Badly?

AUSTEN: Gas poisoning.

MARY: Then hadn't you better see to him?

AUSTEN: A lawyer named Godfrey is with him. But—

MARY: Dr. Cameron will know what to do. (*Hurriedly*) You mustn't leave him in the night air. I'll prepare a room, and . . . and light some lamps, and . . . unbar the front door. You go out the way you came, and bring him to the front door. Do hurry!

AUSTEN: Why are you looking like that?

MARY: Like what?

AUSTEN (*suspiciously*): You . . . it seems foolish to say this, but you don't mean to run away again?

MARY (*bitterly*): Run away? How could I run away? (*As though to herself*) In all the broad earth, where could I run away?

AUSTEN: Oh, Mary, Mary, Mary.

MARY: Please go. I'll close the window.

(*A long pause, after which we hear the sound of squelching footsteps.*)

AUSTEN: Hallo! Mr. Godfrey! Is that you?

GODFREY: At your service, sir. With some effort, I have managed to get your friend across my horse. I am no leech, but I should say his condition was critical.

AUSTEN: We're in luck. This is a doctor's house. Dr. Cameron.

GODFREY (*sharply*) Dr. Horatio Cameron?

AUSTEN: You know him?

GODFREY: I had the pleasure—no, hardly that—of making his acquaintance under somewhat tragic circumstances. At a trial for murder. (*Grimly*) And, later, at the execution. —Did you shiver, sir?

AUSTEN: I don't know. I felt that someone had just walked over my grave. We're to go to the front door.

GODFREY: There do not appear to be any lights in the house?

AUSTEN: Yes, there's a light in . . . (*As though a horrible premonition were coming to him*) No, by God, there isn't!

GODFREY: You had better knock.

(*An iron door-knocker raps loudly. But there is no reply while Austen and Godfrey remain silent.*)

AUSTEN (*uncertainly*): But Mary said . . . that is, the lady I met here five minutes ago . . .

GODFREY (*dryly*): You appear, sir, to have reached intimate terms with the lady remarkably quickly. This infernal mist (*coughs*) is strangling me. Knock again. (*The knocker raps more loudly.*) Ah, that's better! Someone is opening an upstairs window.

DR. CAMERON: Yes? What is it?

GODFREY: Dr. Cameron?

CAMERON: At your service.

GODFREY: You will pardon us for troubling you at this hour, but a gentleman here has met with a serious injury. Will you be good enough to look at him?

CAMERON: One moment.

GODFREY (*puzzled*): Er—you say, sir, that you met the lady of the house five minutes ago?

AUSTEN: I don't know whether she's the lady of the house. Miss Adair—

GODFREY (*startled*): What name did you say?

AUSTEN (*fiercely*): Miss Adair. Mary Adair. She is—or was—in the drawing room.

GODFREY (*breathing*): God help us!

AUSTEN: What's wrong? Why do you cross yourself?

GODFREY (*querulously but with a tinge of fear*): I might remind you, sir, that the night is damp, that I am subject to rheumatic attacks, and that the effects of iced punch at the Bell Inn have long ago worn off. (*Warmly*) I consider, therefore, that jests on that subject, however witty, are singularly ill-timed . . . (*With relief*) Ah, here's someone at the door.

(*There is the rattle of a bar, and the door opens.*)

CAMERON: Stand forward. Under the lantern where I can see you.

GODFREY: You can put by your pistol, Dr. Cameron. We are not thieves. Perhaps you remember me? Elias Godfrey, at your service.

CAMERON (*politely*): I believe I have some recollection of your face, Mr. Godfrey. Where is the patient?

AUSTEN: I've stood about enough of this foolery.

GODFREY (*nervously*): Now, now!

CAMERON (*as though with raised eyebrows*): Is your young friend also unwell, Mr. Godfrey?

GODFREY (*hastily*): An acquaintance, sir; a mere acquaintance. We met on the road in . . .ah . . . somewhat unusual circumstances. His experiences at your house seem to have been equally unusual. (*As though forcing out the words*) He claims to have been speaking with Mary Adair.

(*Pause.*)

CAMERON (*slowly, in his deepest voice*): There are some jokes, young man, that are not permitted here.

GODFREY: So I told him.

AUSTEN (*almost tenderly*): No, gentlemen, you won't manage it this time.

CAMERON: I don't think I—?

AUSTEN: I mean that this time you—all the pack of you—can't shake your heads sadly and say it didn't happen. Doctor, that girl is in this house, and damned well you know it.

CAMERON (*unheeding*): This is the patient, I think, across the horse. No, Mr. Godfrey, don't trouble. I am of rather powerful build, and I can manage him myself if you will hold the light . . . Stand aside, young man.

AUSTEN: Of course. But I am following you.

GODFREY (*in mental agony*): But perhaps . . . some mistake? Is there any lady in this house?

CAMERON: Only my housekeeper, Mrs. Bragg.

GODFREY: If this young man could . . . ah . . . describe . . .

AUSTEN: I can do better than that. I can show you a painted miniature of her. Look here!

(*A crash.*)

CAMERON: Confound it, sir, can't you manage without dropping the lantern?

GODFREY (*dazedly*): It is not broken. I . . . ah . . . (*pulling himself together*) trust I shall not wake up at the Bell Inn with the fumes of punch still in my head. There also occur to me certain quotations from *Hamlet* which a sensible man . . . (*Finds himself wandering*) May I ask, sir, why you are—or appear to be—interested in this young lady?

AUSTEN: Because I happen to be in love with her. I mean to marry her, if by any chance she'll have me.

GODFREY (*very gravely*): You will not marry her, sir.

AUSTEN: No?

GODFREY: Follow her to the ends of the earth, speak with her every night, in a dream or out of it, and still you will never marry her.

AUSTEN: No? Why not?

GODFREY: Because she is not alive.

AUSTEN (*screaming at him*): Not alive?

GODFREY: I saw her cut down from the scaffold myself. She was hanged for murder more than a year ago.

EPISODE 5

NARRATOR: It is now evening in London, three days later. A lady, discreetly veiled and accompanied by a maid, sits in a private room facing the courtyard of the Bull Inn, Whitechapel. The lady shows signs of impatience.

CYNTHIA (*sharply*): Waiter!

WAITER: Yes, ma'am?

CYNTHIA: Was that the Ipswich coach that arrived then?

WAITER: Yes, ma'am. Just pulled into the courtyard.

CYNTHIA (*hesitating*): I . . . my name is Mercer—Lady Cynthia Mercer

WAITER (*springing to attention*): Yes, my lady?

CYNTHIA: One of the passengers will be a military gentleman—about thirty, rather distinguished looking, long scar across the forehead over the right eye. Will you ask him to come in here?

WAITER: Very good, my lady. Er—would this be the gentleman coming along the passage now?

CYNTHIA: Hugh!

(*Austen's voice is calm but very bitter.*)

AUSTEN: I rather expected to find you here, Cynthia. But I hoped you wouldn't come.

WAITER: Can I get you anything, sir?

AUSTEN: Three pennyworth of brandy and water, Luke.

WAITER: Very good, sir.

CYNTHIA: And you may go, Eleanor. Close the door,

Hugh. (*The door closes.*) Well? What happened?

AUSTEN (*grimly*): Much!

CYNTHIA: You can't imagine what I've suffered. I'm dying to know. Of course I got your letter, but I haven't told a soul about it, because I wanted you all to myself. Hugh, the whole town is agog, positively agog! (*Hesitantly*) And Tommy? What of Tommy?

AUSTEN: He's alive but still only half conscious. I left him at Dr. Cameron's house under the doctor's care. You might tell me what happened to poor old Pepotin. Did he get down alive?

CYNTHIA (*giggling*): The Frenchman? Oh, he's quite safe, poor lamb. He came down, canvas and basket and all, on a bowling green in Essex in the middle of a game. It was dreadful. They chased him with pitchforks.

AUSTEN: Very gratifying.

CYNTHIA: Of course it was very wicked and immodest of me to come here, and I don't know why I trouble my head about either of you, because I'm sure you both got off much better than you deserved. But . . . (*almost wailing*) Oh, Hugh, what happened?

AUSTEN: I found the girl.

CYNTHIA (*incredulously, after a slight pause*): You don't mean that?

AUSTEN: Oh, but I do.

CYNTHIA: The girl from Brussels? You don't mean to say she really exists after all?

AUSTEN (*judicially*): Well, that depends on which side you take. Now I hold that she is a real flesh-and-blood woman, as alive as you are. Mr. Godfrey and Dr. Cameron hold that if I talked to anybody on Wednesday night, I talked to a ghost. (*Bluntly*) The girl in question was hanged for murder more than a year ago. (*Pause*) (*Ironically*) What big blue eyes you have, Cynthia.

CYNTHIA (*wonderingly*): La, the man really is mad now!

AUSTEN: That, my dear, is what I imagined you would say. So I took the trouble to bring along a witness. But before I produce him, let me make the case clear. Mary Adair, aged twenty-five, was nurse-companion to a rich and miserly old woman of eighty. One night in March, the old woman's throat was cut. A butcher knife was used.

CYNTHIA: Don't.

AUSTEN (*remorselessly*): Over a thousand gold sovereigns were stolen out of a bandbox under the bed. They accused Mary Adair. They found blood on one of her dresses. She was duly tried at the Court of Quarter Sessions. On April 12th, 1815, she was hanged outside Aldbridge Gaol in the presence of a crowd who saw her twisting on the rope until she died.

CYNTHIA (*warningly*): Hugh, I shall scream!

AUSTEN: Yes. They say she did too. (*Pause*) Yet I spoke with her on two occasions afterwards.

CYNTHIA (*almost whispering, yet challengingly*): You may think, Captain Austen, that you can frighten a poor weak woman by talking like that . . .

AUSTEN (*gently*): I'm not trying to frighten you, Cynthia. It's true. Just one moment. (*The door opens.*) Mr. Godfrey!

GODFREY (*distantly*): At your service, sir.

AUSTEN: Will you be good enough to come in here, please? (*To Cynthia*) You may as well see the counsel who defended her at the trial. A curious little man, but interesting. (*To Godfrey*) Mr. Godfrey, I should like to present you to Lady Cynthia Mercer. You'll take some refreshment?

GODFREY (*with a cough*): Thank you, no. I seldom touch strong waters. (*Quickly*) Still, if you insist: perhaps a glass of milk punch, well dusted with nutmeg, would prove least injurious to the system . . . (*Sweepingly*) Madam, your most obedient servant!

CYNTHIA (*sniffling*): Yours, sir.

GODFREY: This is a most distressing business.

CYNTHIA: Indeed it is.

GODFREY (*nervously*): And as far as the girl who so unfortunately . . . ah . . . died . . .

AUSTEN (*off-handedly*): She's alive.

GODFREY: Sir, if there were any doubt . . .

AUSTEN: There's no doubt in my mind.

GODFREY (*quietly*): Captain Austen, attend to me. These public hangings, God knows, are a degrading spectacle. One day we may put an end to them. But at least there can be no doubt in anyone's mind as to whether sentence has been executed. Er—I trust I give no offense by speaking of such matters in this lady's presence?

CYNTHIA: I can't even bear to think of such things! —Tell us about it.

GODFREY: There is nothing to tell. I saw the cart drawn from under the unfortunate girl's feet. I saw her hang there for fully five minutes, until she was pronounced dead by Dr. Cameron . . .

AUSTEN: Dr. Cameron!

GODFREY (*quickly*): Why do you say that?

AUSTEN (*groping*): The evil genius. The man in black.

The fellow who denied he had ever seen me before. *He pronounced her dead.*

GODFREY (*with asperity*): My good sir, if you doubt the genuineness of the execution you will drive yourself to Bedlam. I tell you, I saw it. I saw the rope fastened and adjusted around Miss Adair's neck. I saw the hood put over her face. I saw her hands bound behind, and her feet pinioned. I saw—well, do you doubt the genuineness of that?

AUSTEN (*half frantic*): I can't. Too many people say the same.

GODFREY: Then what do you suggest? Come, sir! As a man of the law . . .

AUSTEN (*stubbornly, still groping*): Who is this Dr. Cameron? What do we know of him?

GODFREY (*with some hesitation*): A man of substance, I believe. A cultured gentleman. A student of . . .

AUSTEN: Of what?

GODFREY: Of the arts and sciences. Some have said unhallowed arts and demoniac sciences.

AUSTEN (*heavily*): So if by any chance Dr. Cameron had discovered a method of restoring a dead person to life. . .

GODFREY (*gravely*): Sir, you frighten me.

AUSTEN: Is it impossible? I allow it to be unbelievable, but is it impossible? We've seen miracles in our time. If Dr. Cameron has discovered such a method . . .

GODFREY: If he has, my friend, would you still want her?

AUSTEN (*blankly*): I don't understand.

GODFREY: Suppose the cold flesh grows warm again. Suppose the mark of the rope be erased from the neck. Suppose any wizard's work you like. The girl is a con-

victed murderess. Would you . . . ah . . . still want her?
(*Dead silence.*)

CYNTHIA (*distractedly*): It's horrid, that's what it is: horrid.
I really don't know what people are coming to, falling in
love with ghosts, and . . . and . . . (*Confused but with
dawning wonder*) Mr. Godfrey, Hugh really doesn't look
mad or sound mad, does he?

GODFREY: He is quite sane, madam. That is why I am
here.

CYNTHIA (*echoing*): Why you're here?

GODFREY: He may have seen a ghost. He may have seen
a demon revived to life. But he saw something. All that
remains is my question: does he still—?

AUSTEN: Want her?

GODFREY: Yes.

CYNTHIA (*softly*): A convicted murderess, Hugh.

AUSTEN (*deliberately*): She's no murderess; rest assured of
that. Everything they said about her was a lie and a fraud.
(*Wildly*) A damned lie and a filthy fraud . . .

CYNTHIA (*still softly*): Was it, Mr. Godfrey?

GODFREY (*unhappily*): I—?

CYNTHIA: You were her counsel. Was it a lie and a fraud?
Was she guilty? Do tell us!

GODFREY (*hesitating, plaintively*): I was not at all happy
about the affair. No. I am a cautious man, but I may say
that I was not happy. The unfortunate girl appealed to my
sympathies. I might almost say my softer nature. Miss
Adair was a gentlewoman. She had some knowledge of
languages and music, and very pretty ways about her . . .

CYNTHIA (*with intense contempt*): Pfaa!

GODFREY (*coughing*): Unfortunately, the evidence was

strong. Yes. The victim of the crime lived in a house guarded like a fortress against burglars. All doors and windows were found fastened, with no sign of an entry from outside. The watchdog, loose in the grounds, did not bark all night, and we know that dogs bark at the approach of anyone, friend or foe, who approaches from the outside. Aside from Miss Adair and the victim, the only other persons in the house were two maidservants, whom Mrs. Carver (*drily*) . . . a considerate mistress . . . locked in the attic each night.

CYNTHIA (*sharply*): What name did you say?

GODFREY: Carver. Mrs. Henrietta Carver, of the Old House, Ashbridge. The victim

AUSTEN: Did you know her, Cynthia?

CYNTHIA (*catching herself up*): No, of course not! How you do go on! I—I only . . .

AUSTEN: The name has a meaning for you, doesn't it?

CYNTHIA: No.

AUSTEN: It's growing infernally dark in here. We must have lights. I want to see your face. Waiter!

CYNTHIA (*shrilly*): Do stop! You'll disarrange my bonnet. (*Freezingly*) Really, Captain Austen!

GODFREY (*clucking his tongue mildly*): I think sir, that you are adopting a most extraordinary course if you hope to ask a favor from this lady.

AUSTEN (*abruptly*): I beg your pardon.

CYNTHIA (*offended*): I should think so. (*Pause*) A favor from me? What favor?

AUSTEN: We need help, Cynthia. That was why I wrote to you. You have influence. You know everyone in London. The Prince himself said you were (*sardonically*)

the fairest flower in his hiccup garden.

CYNTHIA (*airily*): La, sir, how you do flatter me. Then it wasn't my *beaux yeux* that made you think of me. (*More sharply*) What on earth could *I* do for you?

AUSTEN: We want to open a grave. (*Urgently*) Please wait! It's customary for the bodies of convicted criminals to be disposed of in quicklime . . . afterwards. But hear what happened in the case of Mary Adair. Dr. Cameron— Dr. Cameron: mark that!—made interest with the Governor of Aldbridge Gaol that the body should be decently buried. Permission to open that grave rests with him. And he refuses permission.

CYNTHIA: Well?

AUSTEN (*eagerly*): But if influence were exerted from higher sources . . . (*Changing his tone*) Cynthia, have pity on me! If what we find in that grave is (*with an effort*) bones and . . . what is left of Mary Adair, I have no more to say. I'll acknowledge that I was mad or drunk or seeing a ghost. I'll never look for her again. But if the coffin is empty, then she's alive. Don't you understand? (*Pause.*)

CYNTHIA (*reproachfully*): You would ask me to do that for you?

AUSTEN: Is it so much to ask?

GODFREY: There is reason in what he says, My Lady.

CYNTHIA (*pouting, distressed*): Oh, Hugh, you know I'd do anything in the *world* for you. But . . .

AUSTEN: Then you won't?

CYNTHIA (*gently*): I can't, dear. (*With sudden querulousness*) Never mind why I can't! (*Reproachfully*) Besides, I think it's most unfair and unreasonable to ask me to make such an idiot of myself! And so improper, too. And Prinny! Prinny, of all people! And those horrid Lord Chancellors, or whatever they are, with their wigs and their gowns and their conversation that I declare I could never make head or tail of! Do you think I could do anything with them?

GODFREY (*under his breath*): I think it highly probable, madam.

CYNTHIA: Oh, Hugh, it's absurd!

AUSTEN: I am sorry. I should not have asked.

CYNTHIA (*anxiously*): You do understand, don't you?

AUSTEN: Of course. Please consider it unsaid. (*With an effort*) This district is not altogether safe after nightfall. May I—?

CYNTHIA (*quickly*): That won't be necessary, dear. I have my own carriage. And my maid. And now I must fly, or I shall be late. Good night, Hugh. Good night, dear Mr. Godfrey. Eleanor! Eleanor!

(*Both men murmur. The door opens and closes. There is a pause.*)

GODFREY (*equably*): Will you take snuff, sir?

AUSTEN: No thanks.

GODFREY: And, now I remember it, we have not yet received any refreshment. I dare say you could do justice to some brandy.

AUSTEN (*gloomily*): Yes. About three bottles, I think.

GODFREY (*scandalized*): Oh, tut, tut! Surely the situation calls for no more than two. (*Reflectively*) A most seductive lady. Dark, plump, and fascinating Er—doubtless you are wondering the same thing I am wondering?

AUSTEN: Yes.

GODFREY: I had thought, a few days ago, that the coming of twilight would make me shiver. I had not thought to hear—

(*A woman's scream, piercing but distant, is heard beyond the door.*)

AUSTEN: What was that? (*Pause*) Waiter! Waiter!

CYNTHIA (*distantly*): Whip up the horses! Drive!

(*The rumble and roll of a coach begins and fades away.*)

AUSTEN: Where's that bell? It's too dark to find anything in here. Waiter! (*The door opens.*) Ah, there you are.

WAITER (*breathing heavily*): Excuse me, gentlemen. I—

GODFREY: Look sharp with that candle, man, or you'll have the place afire. Here, set it on the table. Now. What's wrong?

WAITER (*frightened, hoarsely*): I must have had the 'orrors. It was something I saw.

GODFREY: Saw? What did you see? Speak up!

WAITER: Begging your pardon, sir: I'm not rightly sure. You see, it was like this . . .

(*The voice fades.*)

EPISODE 6

NARRATOR: We return to the private parlor at the Bull Inn, with twilight outside and a single candle burning on the table.

GODFREY (*through his nose*): Go on. What happened?

WAITER (*with an effort*): Well, sir, this gentleman 'ere orders brandy and water . . .

AUSTEN: Yes, I ordered it. What then?

WAITER: Well, sire, I was a-bringing it through the coffee room when the door opens and the lady and gent come in.

GODFREY: Go on.

WAITER: I never seen the gent before. He was an old, very thick-set gent in a cocked hat and one of them box-pleated capes. Oh, yes, and he'd got 'air powder on, which most gents don't wear nowadays; and an ugly look about his eyebrows, like.

GODFREY (*breathing*): Dr. Cameron, on your life!

AUSTEN: And the lady? Speak up, man!

WAITER (*uncertainly*): Well, sir, that's just it. The lady tried to turn away, but I see her face in a looking glass. And it couldn't 'a' bin the person I thought it was. (*Hesitates*) I'm a Suffolk man by birth. Sometimes I goes back there, when there's something good afoot.

GODFREY: Like a hanging, for instance?

WAITER (*flatly*): Yes, sir. (*In a different tone*) And it's no good going after her, Captain. She's gone. Leastways, I hope she is. She's just—gone.

AUSTEN: I can wait. Who screamed out there?

WAITER: The other lady. The lady what was in 'ere with you. As soon as she sets eyes on the fair-haired lady, she opens her potato trap and lets out a screech you could 'ear at Aldgate Pump. Then out she runs and almost takes a header over her own skirts. (*Hoarsely*) Begging your pardon: 'ere's the thick-set gent coming along the passage now. Excuse me.

AUSTEN: Bring my brandy, will you? And milk punch for Mr. Godfrey.

CAMERON: And a pot of tea for me, if you will be so good.

AUSTEN (*with ferocious pleasantness*): And the a pot of tea for Dr. Cameron. Come in, Doctor.

(*The door closes. There is a short pause.*)

CAMERON: Well, gentlemen, do you smell brimstone? Do you see any signs of a cloven hoof about me? By the expression on your faces, I should think that you did.

AUSTEN: How did you come here?

CAMERON: By the Ipswich stage, Captain Austen, like yourselves. Having observed that you booked outside places, I booked an inside. That's all.

GODFREY: And . . . ah . . . left your patient?

CAMERON (*heavily puzzled*): My patient?

GODFREY: Excuse me. You have . . . ah . . . denied nearly everything else in this affair. I trust you don't deny you *have* a patient? Mr. Tring?

CAMERON (*enlightened*): Oh, Mr. Tring! He is well on the way to recovery.

GODFREY: Indeed?

CAMERON: Yes. He will be on his way to London tomorrow. (*Reflectively*) By the way, Captain Austen, he is loud and positive about a wager he seems to have made with you.

AUSTEN: What about the wager?

CAMERON: The question is: Did you win it or did he?

GODFREY (*firing up*): My dear sir, surely there can be no doubt that Captain Austen won it. As the evidence was presented to me, Mr. Tring wagered that only one of the two—himself—would get down alive. Well! Captain Austen is very much alive. Therefore, *ipso facto*—

AUSTEN: I don't care a curse who won the wager. Never mind the wager. Dr. Cameron, where's Miss Adair? (*No reply*) I said, where's Miss Adair?

CAMERON (*politely*): I am not accustomed to being addressed in that tone, sir.

AUSTEN (*with equal politeness*): But you are being addressed in that tone, sir.

CAMERON (*musingly, not without mockery*): What a young fire-eater it is! Always becoming involved in quarrels because of— (*A knock at the door*) Yes, yes; what is it? (*The door opens.*)

WAITER: Excuse me, sir; the guard says you left this in the boot.

CAMERON: Ah, my case of pistols. Put it on the table.

WAITER: Very good, sir. (*We hear a rattle of crockery.*) Brandy and water. Milk punch. Pot of tea.

AUSTEN: Here you are: keep it.

WAITER (*fervently*): Thank *you*, sir! (*The door closes.*)

CAMERON (*conversationally*): Quite a snug little parlor. I'll sit down, if you don't mind. (*A long sigh*) I have certain matters to discuss with both of you, and I have been debating them all the way down in the coach. The fact is, gentlemen . . . Will you pass me the milk, Mr. Godfrey? Thank you . . . The fact is, gentlemen, you have begun to make a serious nuisance of yourselves.

GODFREY (*uneasily*): I assure you, Doctor—

CAMERON (*paying no attention*): Even Mr. Godfrey, a reasonably sane man, is now half convinced that a woman whom he saw die . . . (*Rapping it out*) As you acknowledge?

GODFREY: Unhappily, yes.

CAMERON: . . . that a woman whom he saw die, hanged thirty feet above ground with her neck in a rope, is in some fashion restored to life . . . Now the sugar, please.

AUSTEN (*stonily*): We're waiting, Doctor.

CAMERON: Gentlemen, I am a man of some small accomplishments in the realm of science. I cannot tolerate such childish nonsense as that. Therefore I have a difficult decision to make. Either I must confide in you and tell you the truth, or—

AUSTEN: Or—?

CAMERON: Or not confide in you. As I see fit.

AUSTEN: I think you will confide in us, Doctor.

CAMERON: And the why do you think so?

AUSTEN: Because I propose to choke it out of you if you don't.

(*Dangerous pause. Cameron, breathing as though about to say something, seems to alter his mind, and to go on in the same reflective, unheeding, suave way.*)

CAMERON: So I sit here, and I stir my tea, and I ask myself which is the wiser course. Captain Austen I think I could trust. But Mr. Elias Godfrey is notoriously the worst gossip on the Midland Circuit—

GODFREY (*outraged*): Sir, I most emphatically protest against such an abominable—

CAMERON: —and, with the best intentions in the world, he might betray me before the time is ripe. (*Thoughtfully*) Yes, the choice is difficult.

AUSTEN (*desperately*): What choice? What does all this mean? What are you aiming at?

CAMERON: My life, young man, is nearly over. There is little more for good or evil that I can do. But one thing I can do, and mean to do; and this is what I aim at: (*With sudden, slow fierceness*) That a damned villain may be brought to justice and a great wrong set right before all men.

(*There is a sharp knocking at the door.*)

GODFREY (*plaintively*): Is that the waiter again? Really, we seem to have no more privacy than—

(*The door opens and closes.*)

AUSTEN: Cynthia!

CYNTHIA (*poised but faintly nervous*): Pray don't get up! ... well, if you *must*! Do excuse me for intruding, but I'm almost *certain* I left my reticule behind on the table here.

AUSTEN: I don't see it anywhere.

CYNTHIA (*with surprise*): Oh, dear, don't tell me I *didn't* leave it here after all?

CAMERON (*dryly*): Evidently not.

CYNTHIA: And . . . forgive me: haven't I seen you before?

CAMERON: I believe so, madam. In the coffee room, a quarter of an hour ago.

CYNTHIA: No! I meant . . . before that?

CAMERON: Not unless you saw me when you were a small child. I spent much time in London long ago.

CYNTHIA: But not now?

CAMERON: No. Not since Nash has changed its face. (*Grimly*) I have no fondness for your new dandy strutting in Hyde Park in a bright blue coat with brass buttons, with a cravat so stiff he can't see his own shoes, and manners so bad he even sneers at himself in a looking glass. Nor did I expect the day when Lord Wellington would be seen entering Almack's in trousers.

CYNTHIA: Surely, sir, it would be much more surprising if he were seen entering Almack's without them.

CAMERON: Don't be pert, young lady. I referred to breeches and knee buckles: a civilized custom. (*Pointedly*) And in *my* day, too—

CYNTHIA: In your day, you were about to say, young ladies of good character did not go unattended to public inns.

CAMERON: I leave the question of character to Your Ladyship.

CYNTHIA: You know me, then? (*No reply*) You do know me! I . . . Oh, Hugh, I can't endure this any longer! I *did* make an excuse to come back! This girl of yours—she *is* real. I recognized her from the miniature. She was with this man only a few minutes ago.

AUSTEN: We know that, Cynthia. This is Dr. Cameron—the famous "man in black."

CYNTHIA: I—I thought it must be.

CAMERON: So you know me as well. And we have another person who is interested in the case of Mary Adair?

CYNTHIA: I think it's perfectly horrid. She cut some old lady's throat with a butcher knife.

CAMERON: So it was alleged.

CYNTHIA: Well, didn't she?

CAMERON (*urbanely*): This tea is surprisingly good. In my younger days, tea was the only beverage we could *not* get at Carlton House. I developed a great fondness for it. Can I tempt you to join me, Lady Cynthia?

CYNTHIA (*holding herself in*): No, thank you.

CAMERON: A pity. Ladies have not taken to drinking spirits in these days, I hope?

CYNTHIA (*pertly*): We drink what we please, sir.

CAMERON (*musingly*): And yet have times changed so much, I wonder? I read in the *Times* newspaper that Captain Austen's friend, Monsieur Pepotin, had caused something of a sensation in the country when he descended by parachute. It is only ten years ago—don't you remember—when we were waiting for Boney to invade us with balloons and soldiers fastened to great kites. It is not surprising that they chased Monsieur Pepotin with pitchforks.

CYNTHIA: Dr. Cameron, *may* I have your attention?

CAMERON: With pleasure.

CYNTHIA (*severely*): If in your day, Dr. Cameron, they tried to change the subject as clumsily as you are doing, it's no wonder their womenfolk saw through them.

CAMERON: I stand rebuked.

CYNTHIA: We were speaking about Mary Adair. You do know her, don't you?

CAMERON: No.

CYNTHIA (*despairingly*): What's the good of saying that, when I *saw* you with her not fifteen minutes ago?

CAMERON (*with maddening urbanity*): This tea—

AUSTEN (*heavily and quietly*): Just a moment, Cynthia. If Dr. Cameron doesn't care to acknowledge that, perhaps he'll admit something less damaging. *Did* you know Mary Adair, sir?

CAMERON (*drawing a deep breath*): Yes, I knew her.

GODFREY: Before she was . . . ah . . .?

CAMERON: Before she was hanged by the neck until she was dead.

CYNTHIA: How on earth can she be dead when I saw her? (*Helplessly*) Unless it's someone who looks like her? Unless there are two of them?

AUSTEN: That won't do.

CAMERON (*coolly*): Why not, young man? Isn't it more reasonable than assuming what you do assume?

AUSTEN: Then produce her. (*Silence*) You can't do that, can you? Or at least you won't. No, Cynthia. It isn't quite as simple as that. There is only one Mary Adair, and she is the girl of the miniature.

CYNTHIA: Anyway, she's a common little thing, isn't she, Doctor? Brought up by mountebanks or something?

CAMERON (*in an odd voice*): Why do you ask that?

AUSTEN (*quickly*): You've stung him, Cynthia. I wonder why.

CYNTHIA (*surprised*): I meant nothing by it. Except that if Hugh doesn't get over this insane infatuation of his, heaven knows what will happen to him. He wants to marry a murderess. A common murderess!

GODFREY (*under his breath*): Certainly not a common one. Not a common one, at any rate.

CAMERON (*politely*): You spoke, Mr. Godfrey?

GODFREY: I am not happy.

CAMERON: Nor should you be, my friend.

CYNTHIA: Do you expect anybody to be (*mimicking*) happy? This wretch of a girl cut Mrs. Carver's throat and stole her money . . .

CAMERON (*sternly*): One moment.

CYNTHIA: Well, didn't she?

CAMERON: Since you seem aware of the more grisly details, perhaps you won't mind if I comment on them. May I say that one of the most curious features of the trial was the lameness of the defense conducted by Mr. Godfrey here?

GODFREY (*with hurt dignity*): You may say so if you like, sir. I did my humble best. (*Despondently*) But I was not happy. I—

CAMERON: For instance, isn't it remarkable that not one penny of the money—the thousand guineas—has ever been found?

GODFREY: Yes.

CAMERON: Despite the most thorough search in the house and out of it?

GODFREY: I made the most of the point, sir; I assure you I made the most of the point. But the jury were convinced by the evidence of the locked house and the dog.

CAMERON: Principally the dog, I think?

GODFREY (*in agony*): If you like. But consider! The dog did not run away and could not be lured away. He was a-prowl all night. If any person, friend or foe, had either approached or left that house, he would have made the heavens fall with his barking. That was his habit. A hundred people could swear to it. And when you consider the bloodstains on Miss Adair's gown . . .

CAMERON: One moment!

GODFREY: I merely—

CAMERON: One moment, please. The crime was committed on the night of Tuesday, March 8th. That is correct?

GODFREY: Perfectly correct.

CAMERON: Mrs. Carver's dead body was discovered on the following morning by Mary Adair herself?

GODFREY: Yes.

CAMERON: Miss Adair went to wake her employer at the customary hour, five o'clock, and found—what she found. This brought on a screaming fit. A carter, driving past immediately outside, heard the screams begin, heard the dog start to bark for the first time, and investigated. He and Miss Adair sent one of the maidservants to fetch the authorities, and waited until they arrived. That is a correct resume of the events?

GODFREY: I believe so.

CAMERON: And you still are unable to perceive the defense that would have saved Mary Adair's life?

GODFREY (*shaken*): No.

CAMERON: Ah, well. (*With a long breath as though rousing from a reverie*) However, I have interrupted you too long. I must get along to Stephen's Hotel. Hat . . . cloak . . . gloves . . . And I must not forget my case of pistols. I have a fancy to try my hand at a wafer tomorrow at Joe Manton's shooting gallery. If . . . (*Sharply*) What are you doing, Captain Austen?

AUSTEN: I'm locking the door.

CYNTHIA (*crying out*): Hugh, for heaven's sake, don't do anything foolish!

CAMERON (*ironically*): Captain Austen, for some time I've been watching you sitting there, never saying a word, doubtless thinking long, long thoughts. (*Slowly*) They are dangerous, and actions are still more dangerous. Will you unlock that door?

AUSTEN: Will you tell me what you've done to Mary Adair and what all this means?

CAMERON: No.

AUSTEN: Then the door stays locked.

CAMERON (*warningly*): These are very fine pistols, Captain Austen.

AUSTEN: That is the second time this week I've been threatened with one. They don't impress me. (*Blankly*) Nothing impresses me much, now.

CAMERON: May I ask what you mean to do?

AUSTEN: I'm coming to take your barkers away from you. If you fire, you fire. If you miss, God help you. I mean to have the truth out of you before you leave this room.

CYNTHIA: Hugh, don't be a fool! (*Wildly*) Think of me! Think of the scandal! Think of—

AUSTEN (*wearily*): Cynthia, I'm at the end of my tether. This man is making mysteries for the sheer joy of making mysteries. I can't run after Mary up and down every street in London. But I can get the truth out of him.

CAMERON (*harshly*): I warn you—

AUSTEN: Here I come, Doctor.

GODFREY: Gentlemen, gentlemen, I implore you to stop and consider the consequences that are likely to—

AUSTEN (*through his teeth*): Why don't you fire, Doctor?

GODFREY (*gibbering*): —to follow this most unseemly and indeed dangerous exhibition of—

AUSTEN (*pouncing*): Got you!

CAMERON (*bursting out*): You young puppy, I'll show you whether you can handle me like that!

CYNTHIA (*screaming*): Look out! Look—

(*A sharp pistol shot, then dead silence.*)

CAMERON (*badly hurt in the chest*): You . . . young . . . fool.

CYNTHIA (*moaning*): Hugh, you've shot him. You've *shot* him. (*Her voice rises to a note of incredulous horror.*)

GODFREY: It was an accident. Most distinctly an accident. Here let me help you to a chair, sir. My handkerchief, to staunch that blood.

AUSTEN: Whatever it was, it's done now. Will you tell me the truth?

(*Cameron speaks in such a voice that they are instinctively silent. He speaks slowly, punctuating the recital with gasps; without anger but with intense bitterness.*)

CAMERON: Listen to me, you infernal idiot. *I* saved Mary Adair's life.

AUSTEN: You—

CAMERON: She's not dead. She never was dead. I saved her life with nothing more than a simple conjuring trick that deceived every man-jack of them. (*Gasps*) For a year I've been laboring to get justice for her, and find the person who really killed Mrs. Carver. And, just when I *have* found the person and *am* ready to prove it (*gasps*) you ruin everything by giving me (*coughs*) a bullet in the lung. Mary Adair loves you. But you'll never have her now. You'll hang, d'ye hear? *You'll hang.*

EPISODE 7

NARRATOR: Joe Manton's shooting gallery in Davies Street. June the twentieth, eighteen hundred and sixteen. To Manton's come the sporting gentlemen who wish to "try their hands at a wafer"; that is, pistol practice. The gallery itself, lighted by a grimy glass roof, is now empty except for three dandies who lounge in cane chairs at one end—their legs over the arms of the chairs, their tall hats over their eyes.

FIRST DANDY (*surprised*): What's that, old boy? Not Austen again?

SECOND DANDY (*languidly*): Regular sparkler, ain't he? What's he done this time?

THIRD DANDY: He's shot somebody.

FIRST DANDY: Shot somebody? Duel, you mean?

THIRD DANDY (*greedy but worried*): On my honor, I can't find out the right of it. There was a row in a public house. He shot some old buffer named Cameron, but there wasn't any question of an honest duel. It looks bad for him. It had something to do with this girl of Austen's.

FIRST DANDY: What about her?

THIRD DANDY: She's dead.

FIRST DANDY: Eh?

THIRD DANDY: Or she's not dead. Nobody knows. It seems she was hanged a year ago, hanged by the neck as dead as John Bellingham—but she's alive now.

SECOND DANDY (*in consternation*): Damme, old boy, you're not well.

THIRD DANDY: Gospel truth! And I'll tell you something else. Tommy Tring is back in London, and (*sinking his voice*) he refuses to pay his wager to Austen.

SECOND DANDY (*dazed*): No!

THIRD DANDY (*horrified*): Tommy Tring refuses to pay a debt of honor?

THIRD DANDY: He says Austen didn't win it.

FIRST DANDY (*thoughtfully*): I suppose he can afford to pay it, can't he?

SECOND DANDY: Gad, yes, old boy! He's filthy with the rhino. Got a rich aunt somewhere . . . (*Reflectively*) Come to think of it, though, did you ever know Tring to lose a wager before?

THIRD DANDY: Sh-h! Be quiet. I thought I saw him, too.

FIRST DANDY: Tring?

THIRD DANDY: Yes! (*In a whisper*) Coming out of Joe Manton's office. Pale as a ghost, but (*with an admiring moan*) gad's life, how that fellow can tie a cravat! (*Aloud, effusively*) My dear Tommy! How are you?
(*Pause.*)

TRING (*quietly*): Did I overhear you gentlemen mention my name?

THIRD DANDY (*innocently*): Did we, old boy. Not that I'm aware of.

TRING: You're quite sure of that?

THIRD DANDY: Of course, old boy; we were just . . . er . . . congratulating you on your fortunate escape, and . . . (*Floundering*) You're well, I hope? Everybody is well? How's your aunt?

(*Pause.*)

FIRST DANDY (*under his breath*): What's the matter with the fellow?

TRING (*in a repressed voice*): Oblige me by clearing out of here. All of you.

THIRD DANDY: But—

TRING: Didn't I make myself perfectly clear?

SECOND DANDY: Oh, well, if any gentlemen don't want our company! Come along, Phil. Come along, Billy. (*Still more languidly as his voice fades*) D'ye know, if I hadn't an important engagement with a lady, I should resent the fellow's tone. I . . . (*The voice fades away.*)

TRING: That's better. Now I want Joe Manton. (*Calling*) Joe! Where the Devil are you?

(*Manton answers. He has a brisk, competent, far-from-obsequious voice.*)

MANTON (*distantly*): Coming, sir. (*As he approaches*) I was looking for you, Mr. Tring.

TRING: Joe, do you think I'm the best shot in London?

MANTON: No, sir, not the best. But your shooting is respectable.

TRING (*whimsically*): Precisely what you told George Byron, eh?

MANTON: Much the same, sir. I find it pays to be honest with you gentleman, and then you don't go making foolish wagers.

TRING (*sharply*): What do you mean by that?

MANTON (*surprised*): Nothing, sir. Only what I said.

TRING: Look here. I've had an unpleasant experience with coal gas. I want to try a few rounds with the light barkers to see if my eye's still good. I have (*significantly*) some work to complete.

MANTON: Very good, sir. But I wanted to tell you. There's a lady outside in a vis-a-vis carriage, asking to see you. She can't come in here, of course.

TRING (*groaning*): Oh, Lord! Cynthia Mercer! Tell her I can't—

MANTON: No, sir, it isn't Her Ladyship. I never saw this lady before. A fair-haired lady.

MANTON: This way, please. (*The voice fades for a second.*) There you are, sir; across the street. The black carriage with the silver hammer cloth. Excuse me.
(*Pause.*)

TRING (*clearing his throat*): You sent for me, madam?
(*Mary speaks. Her voice is almost without expression.*)

MARY: Yes. Will you get into the carriage, please? . . . Thank you.

TRING: I don't think I have had the honor—?

MARY: No, you've never seen me before.

TRING: I could see you better if you were to raise that veil.

MARY: There! Does that satisfy you?
(*Tring draws in his breath.*)

TRING: I'm certain I've seen you somewhere before. At Lady Jersey's, was it?

MARY: (*Laughs*)

TRING: Why do you laugh?

MARY: Drive on, Robert. Wherever you like. (*We hear the faint clopping of hoofs.*) Mr. Tring, I was born in a traveling fair and brought up among jugglers and gypsies and mountebanks and other good friends. I might have been the little girl you threw a penny to from your fine pony. When I was sixteen, an old lady named Carver, Henrietta

Carver, took me away from the fair and gave me some education. She was very kind to me, in her way.

TRING (*bored*): Well, madam, this is all very interesting no doubt, but I don't see how it concerns me.

MARY: No?

TRING (*amused*): You're still making public appearances, I gather?

MARY: On my last public appearance, thousands of eyes watched me.

TRING (*flatly*): Indeed.

MARY: They watched greedily for every twitch of my body, every jerk of my bound hands, every drop of agony that could be squeezed from the show. And I suffered it. On my last public appearance, I was hanged at Aldbridge.

TRING (*offhandedly*): Do you mind, madam, if I find this joke in very poor taste?

MARY: Joke? But I'm not joking.

TRING (*half humorously*): I gather, at least, that you were not—disposed of?

MARY: Oh, yes. They convicted me for the murder of Mrs. Carver. Would you care to hear about it?

TRING: If it would not distress you too much.

MARY: Mrs. Carver had her throat cut on the night of the eighth of March. A thousand gold sovereigns were stolen out of a bandbox under her bed. Mrs. Carver and I were alone in the house, except for two maids who were locked up in the attic. So they said that I did it, you see, because nobody else could have done it.

TRING: Oh?

MARY: It was really the dog that convicted me. We had a watchdog outside—Tempest, his name was—whose habit was to bark and bark and bark if anybody stirred during the dark hours, either approaching the house or leaving it. He was a dreadful dog, Tempest was. You couldn't even open a window without rousing him. But all night long Tempest never barked . . . until I discovered Mrs. Carver's body at five o'clock in the morning and began screaming. So they knew that no outsider could have crept in and killed Mrs. Carver. (*Slight pause*) I thought this part of the story would particularly interest you, Mr. Tring.

TRING: Indeed? Why so?

MARY: Didn't you tell Captain Austen during the balloon journey that you were experimenting at the Royal Academy with the effect of opium on animals? (*Slight pause*) But no matter. They said I did it. They kept me in a foul hole underground. They would not even let me wash before my execution: a poor humiliation but a terrible one. And then, one morning, they hanged me.

TRING (*dryly*): Indeed? With a real rope and a real noose?

MARY (*still unemotionally*): Yes.

TRING: And yet you didn't die?

MARY: No.

TRING: Then, damme, madam! —All I can say is that the performance deserves to be exhibited to an even larger audience. I'm sure the Theatre Royal would be interested. I can give you a card to the manager, if you like.

MARY (*thoughtfully*): Is that all it means to you, Mr. Tring?

TRING: Yes, I'm afraid so. (*Coolly*) After all, I don't know you, do I?

MARY: You're sure that's *all* it means to you?

TRING: Why should it mean anything to me?

MARY (*gently*): But Mrs. Carver was your aunt, wasn't she?

(*Tring draws in his breath. There is a long pause while we hear the clop-clop of horses' hoofs.*)

MARY (*insistently*): Wasn't she, Mr. Tring?

TRING: A—a devilish unfortunate business, I know. I—I haven't told anyone about her death. It didn't seem necessary to dwell on it. You know how it is in London. Very few people even know my aunt's name, much less that she ... came a cropper like that, poor old girl.

MARY: Lady Cynthia Mercer knows her name. And you mentioned her to Captain Austen during that balloon journey. You mentioned her still more when you were lying in delirium at Dr. Cameron's house.

TRING (*unconcerned*): Did I?

MARY: Yes. And it still means nothing to you? Agony, shame mean nothing to you?

TRING (*testily*): My dear lady, what do you expect me to do? Summon one of the Charlies and have you arrested all over again? (*Warningly*) They won't make the same mistake twice, you know.

MARY: No, they won't make the same mistake twice. But you asked how all this concerned you. Tell me: were you at that shooting gallery practicing to ... to ...

TRING: To call out Captain Austen? Yes.

MARY (*in a repressed voice*): That won't be necessary.

TRING: Why not?

MARY: Because Captain Austen will be lucky if he escapes death or transportation to the colonies for life. (*Holding herself in*) He ... he quarrelled with Dr. Cameron last night. There was a scuffle. A pistol went off. Dr. Cameron is dead.

TRING (*softly*): Is he, by Jove?

MARY: There were two people in all this world who believed I didn't kill Mrs. Carver, and shared my secret. One of them is dead and the other . . .

TRING: Safely disposed of, eh? Most unfortunate. And now the secret is shared only by you and me.

MARY: Yes.

TRING: Of course, you *did* kill Mrs. Carver?

MARY: You know I didn't.

TRING: Explain that, please.

MARY: Dr. Cameron suspected who the real murderer was. But he died before he could tell us how he meant to prove it.

TRING: I see. Did Dr. Cameron tell you whom he suspected of being the murderer?

MARY: Yes.

(*Again we hear horses' hoofs during a silence.*)

TRING: And just why are you tell me all this, dear lady?

MARY: I thought we might come to terms.

TRING: Perhaps we might. I don't say yes; I don't say no. I don't commit myself. However, by a curious chance your driver—who seems to be lending an attentive ear to all this—is passing the neighborhood of my lodgings. Would you care to take a glass of sherry with me while we discuss it?

MARY: I might.

TRING: It wouldn't compromise your reputation?

MARY: Can a woman who has been hanged have her reputation compromised much further?

TRING (*unruffled*): True. I forgot that. And you're not afraid of me?

MARY (*bursting out with intense low-voiced fury*): Of you?

You perfumed, lackadaisical *swine*!

TRING: You may regret that remark, you know. (*Calling*) Stop here, driver. That's right. Allow me to assist you down, madam ... There! You may go, driver. (*The carriage moves off.*) How quiet these squares are at this time in the evening. Except, as I live, for a full-fledged Bow Street Runner tethering his horse to the rail. This is a light and sign from heaven ... that is, if I discover you're telling the truth. (*Calling*) Halloa, there! You!

THE RUNNER (*in a hoarse voice*): Yus? What's o'clock?

TRING: Come here a moment, will you?

MARY: What do you mean to do?

TRING: I had no intention of entertaining you in my lodgings, dear lady, but I was obliged to separate you from your driver ... (*To the Runner*) Charlie, my name is Tring. Thomas Tring.

THE RUNNER (*with interest*): Ow?

TRING: Yes. I've just heard some distressing news. I've heard that a friend of mine, a certain Dr. Cameron, was shot last night in a brawl, and that the man who shot him was another friend of mind, a Captain Austen. Is that true, do you happen to know?

THE RUNNER: I dunno 'oo give you the wire, but I don't mind tellin' you it's true enough.

TRING (*under his breath*): So you weren't lying!

MARY (*under her breath*): What do you mean to do?

TRING: Then it will interest you to know, Charlie, that I've got another prisoner for you.

THE RUNNER: Oh?

TRING: Yes. This woman here ... No, you don't, you vixen! ... I give her in charge myself. The authorities in

Suffolk will be glad to hear she's alive. She slipped through your fingers once before, and you must be careful she doesn't do it again. (*With interest*) Ah? I see you've got handcuffs?

THE RUNNER (*heavily*): These 'ere gyves ain't for the lady.

TRING: Not for the lady? Then who are they for?

THE RUNNER: Well, my bucko, not to put too fine a point on it, they're for you. (*Snarling*) Stand fast or I'll let daylight in you!

TRING (*shrilly*): What does this mean? What are you doing to me?

THE RUNNER (*formally*): Thomas Tring, I've got 'ere a warrant for your arrest on a charge of murderin' your aunt, Henrietta Carver, on the night of March 8th, eighteen hundred and fifteen. This warrant was swore out by Dr. Horatio Cameron, the gent as is standin' on the doorstep just behind you now . . .

MARY (*softly*): Hello, guardian. I brought him home, you see.

THE RUNNER: . . . and also by Captain Hugh Austen, as is standin' beside Dr. Cameron there and lookin' at you in a way that *I* shouldn't like to 'ave looked at me.

MARY: Hello, Hugh darling.

THE RUNNER: And before takin' you off to Newgate, Thomas Tring, I proposes to allow you 'arf an hour alone in the 'ouse with them two gentlemen, one of whom ain't so badly damaged by the bullet that he can't be uncommon nasty if he should want to try. And meantime I proposes to stand 'ere and smoke me pipe, peaceful like, entertainin' the lady with such light conversation as seems genteel and proper to the occasion.

EPISODE 8

NARRATOR: And so, with the arrest of Thomas Tring for the murder of Henrietta Carver, the crime for which Mary Adair was wrongly sentenced—and in some unknown fashion escaped death—we approach the end of our tragic comedy. It ends, as it began, in Carlton House, home of the Prince Regent. Again there are crowds and wax lights, and flowers and fruit and iced punch. Again Hugh Austen, now more an object of curiosity than ever, has been invited to this august assembly. With him is Mary Adair. We see them in one corner of the gold drawing room as . . .

(The voice fades. The murmur of a crowd rises and then also fades away.)

MARY: I think I'm rather nervous. They stare so, don't they?

AUSTEN *(happily)*: Let 'em stare! Who cares a ruddy farthing? Here, give me your hand. Openly.

MARY *(candidly)*: I don't mind. They say we were only invited here because the Prince is curious about—me.

AUSTEN *(quickly)*: Do you mind?

MARY *(slowly)*: Not now. I did mind, though. Terribly.

AUSTEN: Would you rather go?

MARY: No. I like it. Besides, it's a royal command. And Dr. Cameron will be here to support us. Is the Prince very charming?

AUSTEN: He is, Cynthia Mercer says, the First Gentleman

of Europe.

MARY: I don't see her here tonight. (*Flatly*) She loves Tommy Tring, doesn't she?

AUSTEN (*puzzled*): So I've always believed. But it didn't prevent her from appearing in her box at the theater last night, with Dan Mackinnon hanging over the back of the chair. And if she hadn't told us that Tring was Mrs. Carver's nephew . . . (*Breaking off*) Good Lord! Look there!

MARY: What is it?

AUSTEN: It's Godfrey, Mr. Godfrey! Evidently he was included in the invitation too.

MARY: Doesn't he seem to you to weave slightly in his walk?

AUSTEN (*heartily*): Not at all! An amiable indisposition! Good evening, Mr. Godfrey.

(*Godfrey seems wrapped in profound contemplation, as though shaking his head. He speaks half to himself.*)

GODFREY: Astonishing! Most as-tonishing!

AUSTEN: What is?

GODFREY: I . . .ah . . . refer, sir and madam, to the company here. Yes. When I entered these august portals, I shook in my humble shoes. I expected to see coroneted heads swimming about like ships at a regatta. I expected to see eminent statesmen discussing the affairs of Empire, and eminent literary men discoursing noble thoughts. So far—to recognize—I have counted four jockeys, an opera singer, two pugilists, and a flageolet player . . .

MARY: I'm among my proper companions, then.

GODFREY: . . . and the only literary man present is a Scotchman named Walter Scott, suspected of being the author of *Waverly*, who is reciting Border Ballads on the staircase. Astonishing. However, I feel better.

AUSTEN: Will you join us in a glass of punch, Mr. Godfrey?

GODFREY (*coughing*): Thank you, no. I seldom touch strong waters. Still, if you insist . . .

MARY: Here he comes! The Prince! Coming straight towards us, too! Do I look as tousled as I feel?

AUSTEN: You look lovely, my dear . . . (*As though bowing*) Your Royal Highness!

THE PRINCE: Captain Austen, I believe? Captain Austen, my compliments to you. My most profound (*hiccup*) compliments!

AUSTEN: Your Royal Highness is kind to say so. May I present my fiancée, Miss Adair?

THE PRINCE (*admiringly*): A charming curtsy, b'gad! Charming! Miss Adair, your knee—if I may mention such a delicate subject—is to the manner born.

MARY: Your Royal Highness is too kind.

THE PRINCE: And I congratulate you on your choice of a husband. Captain Austen has had a distinguished military record. (*Expansively*) Gad, it warms the heart of an old campaigner like myself! Captain Austen was at Waterloo, I believe. Now *I* was at Waterloo.

AUSTEN: Indeed, sir? (*Under his breath*) Here it comes.

THE PRINCE (*triumphantly*): Now I dare swear you never recognized me, did you?

AUSTEN: No, sir.

THE PRINCE: It was the (*hiccup*) hat that did it. I had the honor to command . . . not the Guards, as many have thought . . . but the Household Brigade of Cavalry. I'll tell you about it. When we . . . (*Breaking off*) Gad's life, see who's here now!

AUSTEN: Dr. Cameron, you mean, sir?

THE PRINCE (*warmly*): Horry Cameron, the friend of my boyhood days! Though a much older man even then, of course . . . Horry, my boy, this is indeed a (*hiccup*) pleasure! What brings you from the wilds of Suffolk?

CAMERON (*gravely*): You sent for me, sir.

THE PRINCE (*blankly*): I sent for you?

CAMERON: In a way, you sent for all of us.

THE PRINCE: Did I? Why?

CAMERON: You wished to hear the details of the case of Mrs. Carver's murder, and of the girl who was hanged and yet lives.

THE PRINCE (*startled, under his breath*): This is the gel who . . . ?

CAMERON: Yes.

THE PRINCE (*with real dignity*): Madam, I ask your pardon. If I had known that the person in question was anyone so young and charming as yourself, believe me I should never have subjected you to this; much less mentioned the matter in your presence.

MARY: It is of no matter. Please believe that!

THE PRINCE: I was . . . ah . . . I was—ah, yes! (*With a gush of relief*) I was just telling them about my experiences at the battle of Waterloo, where I had the honor to command the Guards. You knew I was at the battle of Waterloo, Cameron?

CAMERON: I believed Your Royal Highness's statement that you *would* be there.

THE PRINCE: Eh?

CAMERON: I believed it to such an extent that *I* took Miss Adair to Brussels in the hope of gaining your ear private-ly. I even had a miniature painted of her for you, knowing you to be kindhearted.

THE PRINCE (*hurriedly*): I was very much occupied, Horry. Very!

CAMERON (*gravely*): So we gathered. But at least, sir, you no longer have any illusions about this man Thomas Tring.

THE PRINCE (*firing up*): He's an infernal villain, that's what he is! Mind you, I've suspected it for a long time. No money of his own, but never lost a wager and never lost at cards . . . I say, Oliphant! Mr. Tring's not to be admit-ted to this house again, d'ye hear?

A VOICE (*whispering*): He's in prison, Your Highness.

THE PRINCE: Ah, yes. So he is. (*Brooding*) Well, send him round some grapes with my compliments. We mustn't be too hard on the poor (*hiccup*) fellow.

CAMERON (*grimly*): You'll forgive us, sir, if we . . . Miss Adair and Captain Austen and myself . . . take a rather less kindly view of Mr. Tring. He deliberately killed a miserly aunt for her hoard of sovereigns. There were even features of cleverness about the crime.

MARY: There were!

CAMERON: The ordinary burglar poisons a watchdog. Just like that! Thereby betraying the fact that he *is* a burglar, coming from the outside. Mr. Tring was cleverer. He drugged the dog's supper with opium in a carefully grad-uated dose so that the effect would have worn off by the early hours of the morning. And the dog couldn't talk. Of course, Tring had many opportunities to steal a key to

Mrs. Carver's house.

MARY: It's odd, you know. I never saw him there.

CAMERON: But he saw *you*, my dear.

MARY: Yes. I—I suppose he did.

CAMERON: And we can now understand Tring's ceaseless persecution of Captain Austen. Can't we, Austen?

AUSTEN: I'm not sure. I can understand why he tried so hard to discredit me and poured ridicule on my story. He didn't want Mary to be found. If she were found, there might be a deeper investigation and his goose might be cooked. But why the attempt to kill me? Why the elaborate balloon challenge? What did he want there?

CAMERON: He wanted that miniature.

AUSTEN: Pardon?

CAMERON (*testily*): My dear boy, he wanted the miniature. If you merely went about giving a verbal description of the girl, which might have fitted hundreds, that couldn't hurt him. But a picture of her! Didn't you tell me your hotel bedroom had been ransacked twice in that week by sneak thieves? But you kept the miniature on your person.

AUSTEN (*reflectively*): By George, that's true! I remember telling Cynthia about it, anyway.

MARY: What *I* can't understand is how he knew I was alive after all. The doctor and I have been terribly careful.

AUSTEN: I can tell you that. He must have seen you at the ball in Brussels. Cynthia Mercer told me he was there. (*Grimly*) He thought you were content to hide and keep out of the way for good. His great danger was that *I* should insist on finding you.

CAMERON: Precisely.

AUSTEN: And you brought him to justice, Doctor.

CAMERON (*amused*): I can hardly claim any credit for that. He gave a full recital of his crime when he was delirious after the gas poisoning. All I *can* claim is that I knew from the first Miss Adair was not guilty.

THE PRINCE (*in a huff*): One moment!

CAMERON: Sir?

THE PRINCE (*very much on edge*): Excuse me. Who is this small person in spectacles who keeps making strange whirring noises in his throat and shifting from one foot to the other? (*As though shooing him*) You, sir! Go away, sir! You make me nervous!

CAMERON: A thousand apologies. This is Mr. Elias Godfrey, a barrister, whom I commend to your notice.

THE PRINCE (*mollified*): A barrister? Ah! Now there you touch me deeply. I have been told that I have some small gift of eloquence myself. I meant no offense, Mr. Godfrey. Will you take a glass of punch?

GODFREY: I—ah—

AUSTEN: Mr. Godfrey seldom touches strong waters, sir. Still, if you insist . . .

GODFREY (*pleased*): A most happy summing up! (*Coughs*) But what I should wish to ask about, if it will not distress Miss Adair, is the reason for Dr. Cameron's certain belief to her innocence.

CAMERON: My dear Godfrey, allow *me* to ask *you* a question or two.

GODFREY: At your service.

CAMERON: What was the date of the crime.

GODFREY: March eighth, eighteen hundred and fifteen.

CAMERON: And the time at which the body was discovered

by Miss Adair?

GODFREY: Five o'clock in the morning.

CAMERON: At five o'clock in the morning, then, it would not yet be daylight?

GODFREY: No.

CAMERON: Miss Adair discovers the body and begins to scream. This attracts a carter who is passing immediately outside. He enters and remains with Miss Adair while they dispatch a maidservant to fetch the authorities. They arrive and promptly arrest Miss Adair. Granted?

GODFREY: Granted.

CAMERON: The entire case for the Crown was based on the assumption that the dog remained awake all night. In fact, it was not even questioned by the defense. *You* believed it?

GODFREY: Yes.

CAMERON: Good. Then, if Miss Adair were the murderess, when and how did she remove the stolen money from the house?

(*Dead silence.*)

GODFREY: I—

CAMERON: Let me elaborate. Over and over again, we have heard of this dog Tempest. He barks at the movement not only of stranger but of friend. He barks not only at anyone approaching the house but at anyone leaving it. He cannot even abide the raising of a window. (*Pause*) Now the stolen money was not in the house. If Miss Adair removed it, as they say she did, she must have removed it between nightfall and five o'clock in the morning. What do we see now? Laden down with a thousand gold sovereigns—no small weight—Miss Adair leaves the house . . . hides the money somewhere . . . *and gets back again* . . . all without a whisper being heard from this famous dog. I am an old fogy, gentlemen. But it does seem to me that this barking dog business cuts both ways.

GODFREY: Inflicting, I fear, something of a wound on my self-esteem.

AUSTEN: But would it have proved her innocence?

CAMERON: No. It would merely have destroyed the Crown's case and set her free.

MARY (*thoughtfully*): Free . . .

CAMERON: Unfortunately, I heard of the affair too late. The sentence was passed and the damage done. So we did—what we could.

THE PRINCE: I won't press you, old boy. But, damme! (*Explosively*) Would you care to say how you managed that act of black magic?

CAMERON (*with distaste*): It was not black magic. It was grotesque foolery. I—I bribed the hangman and the prison governor, of course. The hangman *had* to know. (*Dryly*) You would be surprised to know how much money it takes to buy a common hangman. And now, sir, have we your permission to retire?

MARY (*breathlessly*): Tell them, Doctor. Tell them! If you don't, I will. All I feared was that I should be discovered, and they would *laugh* at me . . . one huge shout of laughter out of those inhuman throats . . . and that they would still be laughing when I really died.

AUSTEN: Don't, Mary!

MARY (*calmly*): Has Your Royal Highness ever seen a traveling circus?

THE PRINCE: Yes.

MARY: I was brought up in one.

THE PRINCE (*startled*): Indeed?

MARY: Then perhaps you've seen those mountebanks who hang by their teeth from wires?

THE PRINCE: Their teeth . . .

MARY: I was taught to do that, among other things, when I was twelve years old. I had yellow curls and a silver-spangled frock.

GODFREY: Miss Adair, I beg of you, don't distress yourself! If—

MARY: They put a bag over your head and face, you know, when they hang you. In a pocket inside that bag, there was a rubber grip to go in my mouth and a metal grip to fasten on the rope as it passed my face. When the hangman pretended to adjust the hood, I fumbled with it too. We caught the metal grip on the rope through the bag. Nobody could see it. Then they bound my hands and feet. It's usual to bind them first of all, you know.

GODFREY: I remember! I told these gentlemen about it! I thought it was unusual when . . .

MARY: Then they drew the support away. When Dr. Cameron judged I couldn't hold on any longer, he had them cut me down.

AUSTEN (*breathing*): My . . . God!

MARY: It—it wasn't easy. The tears were running down my face, and all I could think of was the horrible moment when they discovered me. That would have been the worst humiliation of all: to be *found* like that. But they didn't. And afterwards things went as easy as . . . as a marriage bell, I was going to say. (*Laughs a little*) Dr. Cameron was wonderful.

CAMERON (*almost jeering*): I was wonderful?

MARY: For that, and everything afterwards. Hugh, listen to me! We didn't dare tell you anything at first—

CAMERON (*chuckling*): No. In Brussels I attempted to scare Captain Austen away with all manner of bogey threats. I did not, I am glad to say, succeed.

AUSTEN (*surprised*): You're laughing. I didn't know you ever laughed.

CAMERON (*still more surprised*): You thought me incapable of it?

AUSTEN: Yes, I did, rather.

CAMERON: I bear you no malice for my bullet wound, if that's what you mean. I was a little overwrought that night at the inn. But I couldn't tell you the truth when you challenged me. Lady Cynthia Mercer was there and would have carried the tale straight to Tring. Just as Mary herself could tell you nothing the night you landed in the balloon. You said you had Godfrey with you. And Godfrey, as I have had occasion to remark . . .

GODFREY: Is the worst gossip on the Midland Circuit. (*Grandly*) I forgive it this time. But don't say it again.

CAMERON: What are you thinking, Mary?

MARY: I was wondering what His Royal Highness was thinking.

THE PRINCE: I, madam?

MARY: Yes. I—I'll go, if you like. I know I must seem crude and . . . and silly and . . .

A VOICE (*whispering*): Your Royal Highness.

THE PRINCE: Yes.

VOICE: Supper is served, sir. If—

THE PRINCE (*clearing his throat, very formally*): Miss

Adair, is it your impression that I am (*hiccup*) the worse for liquor?

MARY: Not *much* the worse, sir. Why?

THE PRINCE (*gravely*): If not, perhaps you would accord me the very great honor of taking my arm when we go in to supper?

(*Distantly come the strains of "Auprès de ma Blonde" faintly at first, but gradually rising to the end of the following.*)

MARY (*as though curtsying*): Your Highness's most obedient servant.

THE PRINCE: You will follow us in, gentlemen?

CAMERON: With pleasure.

AUSTEN: With joy and pride.

GODFREY: With humble gratitude.

THE PRINCE: My arm, then, madam. Pay no attention to these idle people who be-clutter our path. They are not to our taste. We of the House of Brunswick may not be witty. We may even be, if this slander can be credited, fat. But, damme, madam! We recognize pluck when we see it, and I tell you that no one woman in a thousand would have had the courage to carry it through as you did. Indeed, it reminds me somewhat of an incident in my own career. Perhaps it would amuse you to hear it. When I, under the pseudonym of General Macleod, commanded the Highlanders at the battle of Waterloo . . .

(*The voice fades away. The strains of "Auprès de ma Blonde" rise to a conclusion and also fade, as we come to—*)

THE END

NOTES FOR THE CURIOUS

The Production

When broadcast on the B.B.C. Home Service weekly between 10 February and 31 March 1941, the cast of *Speak of the Devil* was as follows:

Narrator	*Carleton Hobbs*
Captain Hugh Austen	*James McKechnie*
Lady Cynthia Mercer	*Betty Hardy*
	Lydia Sherwood (Episode 2 only)
Thomas Tring	*Austin Trevor*
Mary Adair	*Belle Crystal*
Dr. Horatio Cameron/The Man in Black	*Cecil Trouncer,*
	Valentine Dyall (Episode 6 only)
Georges Pepotin	*Robert Eddison*
H.R.H. The Prince Regent	*Frederick Lloyd*
Ensign Johnny Brisbane	*Hugh Burden*
Joe Manton	*Arthur Young*
All other parts	*Bryan Powley,*
	Fred O'Donovan, AnthonyHolles,
	Ronald Simpson and *Malcolm Graeme*
Producer	*Val Gielgud*

Thus, in *Speak of the Devil*, we find three actors who achieved fame in the crime and mystery genre: Carleton Hobbs remains to many the definitive Sherlock Holmes for his radio performances on the B.B.C.; Valentine Dyall was, among other roles, that rather better known "Man in Black," the narrator of most of Carr's *Appointment with Fear* series; and Austin Trevor portrayed a clean-shaven Hercule Poirot (!) in three films based on the work of Agatha Christie. Less well known is Cecil Trouncer who, as Dr. Cartaret the coroner, solved many short radio mysteries during the Second World War, written by Carr and others, including Margery Allingham, Freeman Wills Crofts, Gladys Mitchell, E. C. Bentley, and Anthony Gilbert.

People and Places

The man who would rule his country as George IV became Prince Regent in 1811 after the "madness" of his father, George III, was confirmed. His childhood tutor had once said that he would be "either the most polished gentleman or the most accomplished blackguard in Europe—possibly both" and, if "Prinny" never quite lived up to this, he certainly made a good attempt to do so. Before taking the throne, he secretly and illegally married the twice-widowed Mary Anne Fitzherbert, a celebrated figure in London Society. In 1794, he began a liaison with Lady Jersey that ended when he returned to the bosom of Mrs. Fitzherbert after she had the secret marriage verified by no less an authority than the Pope. Despite this and notwithstanding his official but unhappy marriage to Princess Caroline of Brunswick, there were liaisons with Lady Hertford and Lady Conyngham so that it is unsurprising that his achievements as King tend to be somewhat forgotten. "Prinny" also plays a central role in *Fear is the Same* and is mentioned in passing in *The Bride of Newgate*.

The shooting-gallery in Davies Street was managed by Joe Manton until his death when it was taken over by his imaginatively-named son, Joe Manton the younger. Manton Senior is mentioned in *The Bride of Newgate* and his son appears in *Fire, Burn!*. According to Carr's "Notes for the Curious" in that book, "many stories [of the gallery] are told in Captain Gronow's *Recollections and Reminiscences, 1814-1860* (London: John C. Nimmo, 1900)."

Vauxhall Gardens, where, among other fashionable entertainments there were (as noted in *Fire, Burn!* and *The Bride of Newgate*) "fireworks and balloon ascents," were first laid out in 1661 under the name of New Spring Gardens. By 1732 the Gardens had become Vauxhall Gardens and they underwent considerable development before, in 1822, being re-titled the Royal Vauxhall Gardens by George IV. However, by the mid-nineteenth century, the Gardens had lost their once high reputation, and in 1859 they were closed and the site built over.

John Bellingham, whose hanging is mentioned in Episode 7 of the serial, was executed on the 11th of May 1812, for the murder in the House of Commons of the British Prime Minister, Spencer Perceval. According to H. Demoine, writing in *The Eccentric Magazine* in 1814, Bellingham's body was left hanging and, after it had been cut down, his heart was found to "be alive after he was laid open. The expanding and contracting powers continued perceptibly till one o'clock that day." In a sense at least, Bellingham therefore survived the hangman's art, a fact clearly not lost on Carr.

T. M.

ALSO AVAILABLE
from Crippen & Landru

THIRTEEN TO THE GALLOWS
by
John Dickson Carr
and
Val Gielgud

Never before published! Four plays, two by John Dickson Carr alone and two in collaboration with the BBC's Val Gielgud. *Inspector Silence Takes the Air* is set during World War II at an emergency set of studios in a provincial town. There, a murder takes place – and the weapon disappears. In *Thirteen to the Gallows*, also set in a BBC studio, a woman falls to her death from a tower – it is murder, but no one is near her, and the only clue is a scattering of flowers. *Intruding Shadow* is filled with mysteries within mysteries, as Carr expertly shifts the audience's expectations from one suspect to another. *She Slept Lightly* features the ghostly appearances of a young woman during the Napoleonic Wars.

The introduction and notes are by Tony Medawar.

Numbered clothbound, with add'l pamphlet printing a previously unpublished Carr radio script, $43.00

Trade Softcover, $19.00

ALSO AVAILABLE
from Crippen & Landru

Locked Rooms and Other Impossible Crimes

by

EDWARD D. HOCH

Diagnosis: Impossible – The Riddles of Dr. Sam Hawthorne.
>> Trade softcover, $19.00

More Things Impossible: The Second Casebook of Dr. Sam Hawthorne.
>> Signed, numbered cloth edition, $43.00
>> Trade softcover, $17.00

The Ripper of Storyville and Other Ben Snow Tales.
>> Trade softcover, $19.00

The Velvet Touch: Nick Velvet Stories.
>> Trade softcover, $19.00

The Old Spies Club and Other Intrigues of Rand.
>> Signed, overrun cloth edition, $32.00
>> Trade softcover, $17.00

The Iron Angel and Other Tales of the Gypsy Sleuth.
>> Signed, numbered cloth edition, $42.00
>> Trade softcover, $17.00

MORE LOCKED ROOMS
from Crippen & Landru

The Impossible Files of Senator Brooks U. Banner by Joseph Commings, edited by Robert Adey; afterword by Edward D. Hoch.

Cloth, $29.00
Trade softcover, $19.00

The Complete Curious Mr. Tarrant by C. Daly King. Introduction by Edward D. Hoch.

Cloth, $29.00
Trade softcover, $19.00

THE VERDICT OF US ALL
Stories by the Detection Club for
H. R. F. KEATING
Edited by Peter Lovesey
Preface by Dick Francis

Members of London's famed Detection Club have joined together to honor one of their own – H.R.F. Keating, historian of the genre, winner of the Gold Dagger (for best novel) and the Diamond Dagger (for Lifetime Achievement), and creator of one of the greatest fictional sleuths, Inspector Ganesh Ghote.

The Detection Club was founded in 1930 by Anthony Berkeley. Its first Honorary President was G.K. Chesterton, to be succeeded by such luminaries as Agatha Christie, Dorothy L. Sayers, Julian Symons and, for 15 years, Harry Keating. The first American member was John Dickson Carr.

The Verdict of Us All contains **_new_** stories to honor H. R. F. Keating by some of the greatest names in current crime writing:

CATHERINE AIRD

ROBERT BARNARD

SIMON BRETT

LIZA CODY

LIONEL DAVIDSON

LEN DEIGHTON

COLIN DEXTER

JONATHAN GASH

JUNE THOMSON

TIM HEALD

REGINALD HILL

P.D. JAMES

MICHAEL Z. LEWIN

PETER LOVESEY

JAMES MELVILLE

MICHAEL HARTLAND

ANDREW TAYLOR

Numbered clothbound, $43.00
Trade softcover, $20.00

Printed in the United States
217379BV00001BA/6/P